A Painter's Year in the Forests of Bhutan

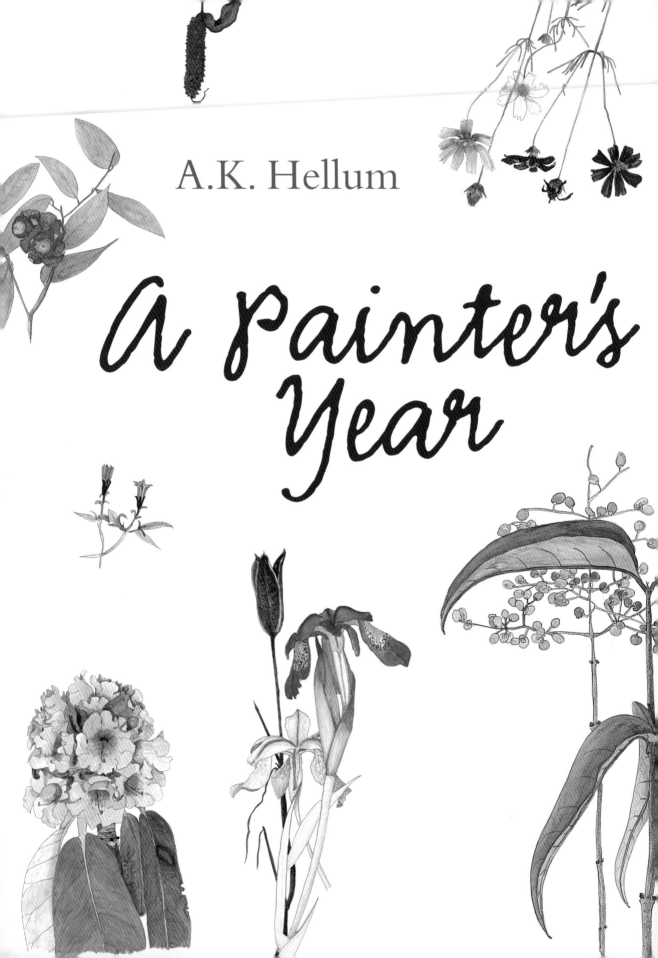

A.K. Hellum

A Painter's Year

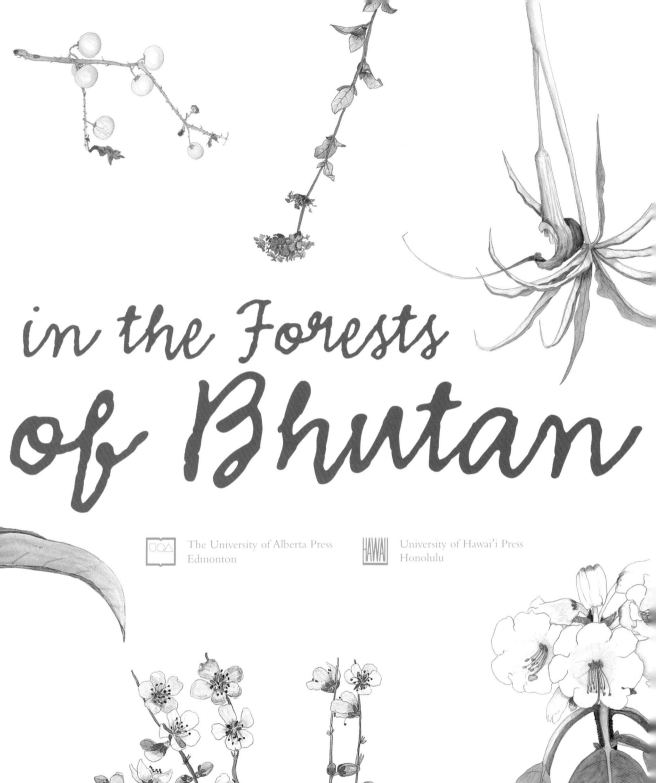

in the Forests
of Bhutan

The University of Alberta Press
Edmonton

HAWAI University of Hawai'i Press
Honolulu

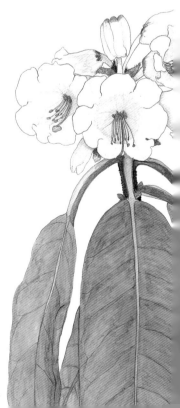

A Painter's Year in the Forests of Bhutan
A.K. Hellum

First Published in Canada by
The University of Alberta Press
Ring House 2
Edmonton, Alberta T6G 2E1

Published in the United States by
University of Hawai'i Press
2840 Kolowalu Street
Honolulu, HI 96822-1888

Copyright © A.K. Hellum 2001
Printed in Canada 5 4 3 2 1

Library of Congress Cataloguing-in-Publication Data

A catalogue record for this book has been requested
ISBN 0-8248-2486-5

Canadian Cataloguing in Publication Data

Hellum, A. K.
  A painter's year in the forests of Bhutan

  ISBN 0-88864-323-3

  1. Hellum, A. K.—Journeys—Bhutan. 2. Botany—Bhutan—Pictorial works.
  3. Bhutan—Description and travel. I. Title.
QK359.6.H44 2001   581.95498   C00-910286-8

The passage that appears on pg. 7 was originally published in *Borealis* 3,1 (1991):43.
The cone drawing that appears on pg. 77 was published previously in *Kuensel* (2 December 1989),
the English-language paper in Thimphu, Bhutan.
The illustrations of *Pteracanthus* sp. (pg. 95)and *Persea clarkeana* (pg. 106) were originally published in
Identification of Some Tree Seedlings in Bhutan. Used by permission.
Photos on pages vi and 120 by T.A. Hellum. Both copyright 1989 T.A. Hellum; used by permission.

Plant taxonomy is a complicated discipline, and nomenclature is constantly changing. Plants in this
book are named using the authorities that were current when the paintings were made; names and
classifications have, in some instances, since changed.

Proofreading by Jill Fallis.
Printed and bound in Canada by Quality Color Press.
Scanning and prepress by Screaming Color Inc.
∞ Printed on acid-free paper.

The University of Alberta Press gratefully acknowledges the support received for its program from the
Canada Council for the Arts. The Press also acknowledges the financial support of the Government of
Canada through the Book Publishing Industry Development Program for its publishing activities.

THE CANADA COUNCIL | LE CONSEIL DES ARTS
FOR THE ARTS | DU CANADA
SINCE 1957 | DEPUIS 1957

Contents

Spring
1

Fall
59

Summer
29

Winter
71

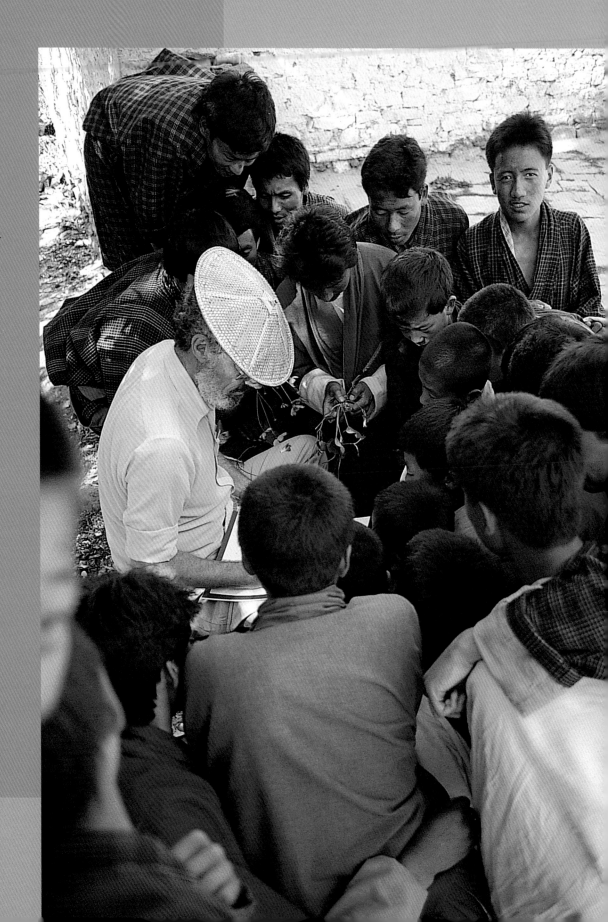

Acknowledgements

This book is dedicated to the common people of Bhutan,

TO THOSE WHO CAME TO SHARE THEIR TIME WITH ME AS I SAT PAINTING. I want to thank the children, the men, the shy women, and the old people who came by and who made my stay in Bhutan such a rich and personal experience. I also want to thank Sonam Tshering, Divisional Forestry Officer with the Department of Forestry, for his help with the identification of many of these plants. His knowledge was invaluable. Finally, I want to thank Leong-Hai Ng and his charming wife, Mindy, for their generous financial help to publish this book. ✳

Introduction

I WENT TO BHUTAN FOR REASONS THAT STARTED IN MY CHILDHOOD.

When I was a child going to elementary school in Norway, there were times when our teacher would tell stories about strange places and peoples living very different lives from ours. I loved those times, because I wanted to live in my imagination, and her voice was gentle. Once, she talked about religions of the world. She told about Borobudur on Java, Angkor Wat in Cambodia, Lumbini in Nepal where the lord Buddha was born, and Taktsang in a country called Bhutan.

It was the name "Taktsang" that stuck in my mind all these years. A holy man called Guru Rimpoche flew in to Taktsang on the back of a tiger and started to meditate in the seventh century. I remember the word *Taktsang*, I think, because it sounds like singing to a rhythm in Norwegian. To me as a child, it conjured up images of monks in red robes singing from rooftops and windows, and high places in the distant mountains, accompanied by monks blowing into long horns, their cheeks bulging like angels' cheeks, and their notes carrying on the winds forever. When the Russian prisoners of war in my home town during the Second World War were allowed to sing their folk songs, I used to think that this was how the monks sounded: sad, mysteriously foreign, very beautiful and full of longing. I remember climbing into the crown of an old beech tree in our yard and sitting there listening, afraid to breathe lest I interfere with my vision of Taktsang. Nearly fifty years passed between my learning about Taktsang and my visit to this special place.

When I first went to Bhutan in the latter half of 1988, it was by Dornier aircraft from Calcutta to Paro, then the only airport in Bhutan. I was at the culmination of a teaching career at the University of Alberta. I felt drained and needed a change. An offer came from an international aid agency to participate in a forest management project in Bhutan. The offer sounded irresistible. The contract lasted two years and entailed helping in matters of forest research and reforestation.

The monsoon rains were abating when I arrived in August, but flights in and out of the country were most uncertain because low clouds often shrouded the land. Landings as well as takeoffs were decided on a moment's notice, if holes in the cloud cover would allow either. The introduction to the country was therefore as secretive and impulsive as the search for treasure, and departures could be equally uncertain.

I completed most of the drawings and paintings in this book in the field as exercises in meditation and concentration. I recorded the stories to commit to paper the situations in which I found myself when painting. People I passed on my way to paint or people passing me while I sat painting created all sorts of events that became integral parts of my life in Bhutan. They gave every painting special meaning. These events gave me the chance to meet people in a way I could not meet them as a forestry consultant.

As the months went by, new plants came into flower or leaf while others faded. Because so much of life revolved around the weather and the seasons in Bhutan, I thought it right to organize the book around their changes. Because I painted year-round, I was left with a whole calendar of feelings that spans two years of magical closeness to nature, and to so many people.

My reason for drawing and painting was not to compile a book of plants for Bhutan—that was far beyond my ambitions. The flora of Bhutan is so very rich it would take many years to illustrate the more than 3,000 vascular plants in the kingdom. My painting and drawing were only tools for meditation. Through concentration on capturing the feelings and looks of plants, my restless mind was stilled for a while.

Even though I devoted almost every one of my weekends for two years, I managed to illustrate only about 150 species and varieties. I did most of my painting in northwestern Bhutan, mainly in the valleys of Thimphu, Paro, Gidakom and Wangdiphudrang, and in the high passes called Chele *La* and Dochu *La*. Altitudes ranged from 2,200 m in the Thimphu valley to about 4,000 m, or just above timber-line, in the Chele *La*.

Despite sun, rain, humidity and freezing temperatures, I finished most of my paintings for this book out of doors, and only occasionally added finishing touches back inside in the evenings or on rainy days when outside work was impossible.

The stories in this book are all true. There are no fancies of the mind. All were the happenings that filled my days with gentleness, so many miracles large and small, and so much human sharing. One would be hard pressed to find a more intimate place than Bhutan to draw and paint.

I was told that when meditating I should focus my mind on temporary things, because life is transient.

Flowers are an ideal medium for such meditation, because what is more transient than the beauty of a flower?

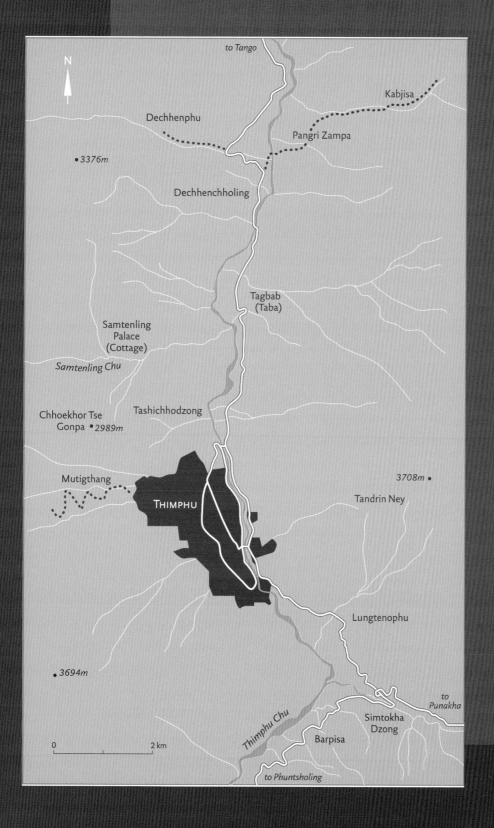

Flora of Bhutan

People of Bhutan to whom I spoke say they feel protective of their plants because they are both rich and vulnerable to misuse. This richness undoubtedly comes from the fact that Bhutan lies between China and India, two very different natural regions, and from its own topographic isolation and highly variable climatic influences from one end of the country to the other. But no one could tell me exactly how diverse the flora is because no one has yet compiled a list. The first edition of the *Flora of Bhutan* is scheduled for completion in Scotland by the year 2000, based on materials collected mainly before the flora project was stopped in the 1980s.

There is no doubt that Bhutan needs a flora, because local plant descriptions are inadequate for separating taxa correctly or adequately. The accidental extermination of plant species surely goes on here as it does elsewhere when no one can take steps to protect given species from overuse or accidental elimination. I have heard that plant collection and identification has again started in Bhutan and that Bhutanese people are being sent abroad to study plant taxonomy and preservation.

People approached me many times because they knew of my botanical interests, asking me when I would make my paintings available in book form. In response to these queries I held two shows in Thimphu and invited people to come and see the paintings for themselves. These events turned out to be popular, judging by the many people who came and who commented favourably on what I had done. I often posted some of my stories with the illustrations, much as I have done in this book. ✳

Rhododendron cinnabarinum

spring

*...the thought of warmer weather
is blissful...*

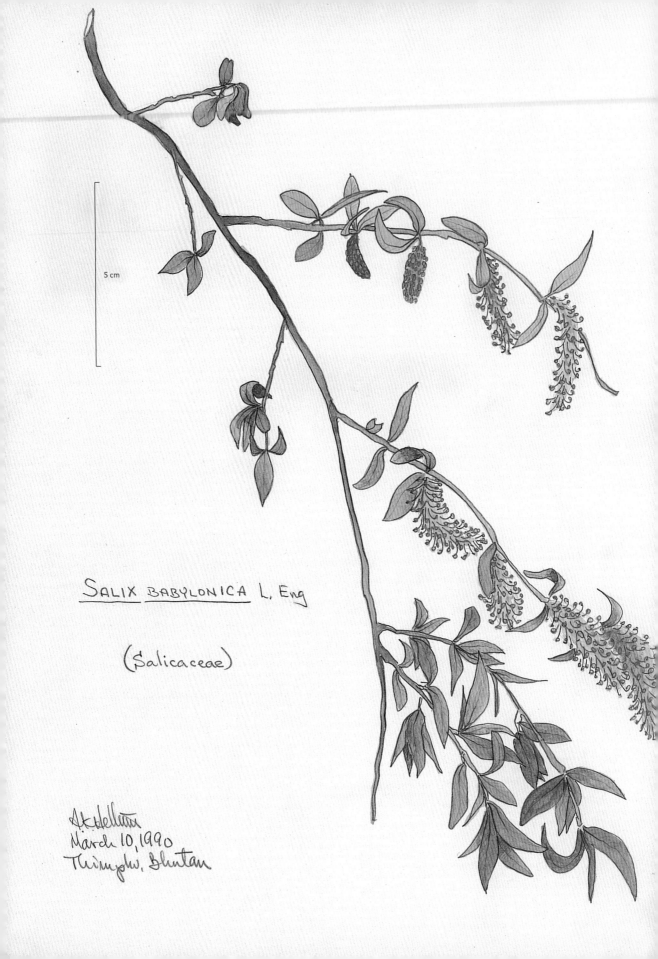

5 cm

SALIX BABYLONICA L. Eng

(Salicaceae)

A. Helluin
March 10, 1990
Thimphu, Bhutan

Spring

SPRING IS AS MUCH A TIME FOR REJOICING IN BHUTAN as it is elsewhere, and the thought of warmer weather is blissful for the ones afflicted with arthritis. Spring comes gradually and the first signs are eagerly sought—such as the first flushing out of the willows in town. From then on the weather gets warmer and nights are milder too. It is then that many people seem to get very busy with preparations for the next growing season, fixing berms along paddy-fields where pigs have rooted, unplugging culverts, and mending aqueducts and channels for irrigation water from the higher hills. Buildings are so cold during winter working hours that some people take their desks outside. When people start again to take their work inside, you know that warmer weather is on the way.

Salix babylonica is the weeping willow of Thimphu. It is found in many parts of the world today. Its catkins, or flowers, emerge before the leaves, and both male and female trees sprout to overflowing with pale yellow-green flowers as early as February. This willow looks nothing like the same species growing in British Columbia, Canada, however, because its bark is blackish brown and irregular, not stringy and orange-brown, and its branches are far less pendant. It is valuable for medicinal and other reasons: its bark contains salicin to soothe aches and pains, and quinine as a prophylactic against malaria. Its branches are used for basketry, the roots can yield blue-red dyes for staining yarns and the leaves from one species can be used for tea. It may be

🐾 *Salix babylonica* L. (spring form)

that this species of willow gave the inspiration for the willow patterns on ceramic wares and may also have been the tree under which the children of Israel mourned and wept. Mabberley (1987) says that willows are associated with sadness because they "weep," but in spring they rejuvenate the spirit in Thimphu and, if anything, sweep away the cold of winter.

The Bhutanese prune willow mercilessly for fodder every year. They trim it severely when it grows too large near buildings and streets. They cut it down and cut its roots in excavations for power and water mains, but it is always there. Its leaves stayed on the tree in late November and into early December 1989, and it flushed again in late February of the next year. Its leaves were golden yellow in fall when its pendant branches were sweeping with the wind, and its flowers and catkins were golden yellow in late February, less than three months later. Only in the coldest of winter months did it stand leafless and grey-black. It was truly a mirror of our longing for spring.

I found the months of December, January and February the coldest in Thimphu. Temperatures go below freezing during the nights, though daytimes can be warm and pleasant. But the houses are draughty and unheated. And if the windows have glass in them, the panes rattle in the thermal winds which blow up the valley every afternoon as if they were pushing day ahead of night.

Between four in the afternoon and nine the next morning, winter seeps into your bones and people huddle around space heaters, small *bukharis*, or wood stoves, and foreigners put on more clothing, buy expensive wood in town, heat their living spaces, and think of the planned trip to Bangkok or Singapore to get warm.

Because the suffering in winter coincides with the leafless stage of the willows, people look so thoughtfully at the golden leaves in fall and say, "The leaves will be gone with the next rain shower or in the next wind. It is winter now."

The gold of the willow is free in this land of simple living. There is nothing you can do to stop it from shedding its leaves or from flowering in spring. But those trees that grow close to the lamp posts and experience continuous light, they hold onto their leaves longest. It is as if the tree is saying, "Go south, go to Punakha, go where it's warm. Don't stay here where it is so cold. We will be here when you return." And that is exactly what the monks do: they move from Thimphu to Punakha every fall and return in spring when the willows look like they have never shed a leaf. Punakha lies about 1,000 m lower in altitude than Thimphu. ✤

The willow is humanity's friend in Thimphu. Its steadfastness is a comfort and an inspiration.

🥀 *Salix babylonica* L. (fall form)

5 cm

SALIX BABYLONICA L. Eng

November 26, 1989
Thimphu, Bhutan

ERYTHRINA ARBORESCENS Roxb.

A.M.Hellum
Wangdi, Bhutan
March 7, 1989.

When you think you are alone

It had started to rain and my painting of Erythrina was quickly put away. This thorny plant is grown in hedgerows, as natural fences for cattle, and it has the most gorgeous crimson flowers in later spring. I rushed to the car and got inside in such a hurry I didn't notice the monk coming towards me on the road, his head held high, shaven clean, his robe that splendid deep wine-red of the Kardgyudpa sect of Buddhists of northwestern Bhutan, his bare feet in flip-flops now covered in mud and bits of plant debris. He walked with pride, water running off his head in streams. He looked cold, his jaw set to contain what might be a building chatter in his teeth, muscles tight in his cheeks. "*Kusesambo*," he said, bending slightly to look into the car through the window. I nodded to him to get in. He smiled then and got in on the passenger side.

"Are you going to Dechhenchholing?" he asked once seated. His use of English was flawless, his pronunciation good. "I am going to Taba," I said. He nodded and sat in silence. When we were moving, rolling down the hill from Hungtso towards Simtokha and Thimphu, he said: "You live in Taba." I nodded and he continued: "I know your house. You like Taba?" I nodded again.

He startled me by adding: "May I see your painting?"

He obviously knew what I was about, but who was he? How strange for a monk to ask—monks were not known so much for their asking as for their ability to listen. I pulled over to the side of the road, fished out the unfinished painting, handed it to him and said, "How did you know I paint?"

"We all know," he said seriously. "Tell me why you paint." I told him of my need to focus my dispersed mind, and he looked very serious when he said, "How do you do this?" I was again taken aback by these forward questions so uncommon for any Bhutanese I had ever met before.

When I told him the paintings were only vehicles to concentration, and not ends in themselves, he nodded and sat silently for the rest of the trip. I drove him to Dechhenchholing because the mountain rains were also falling at Taba and it was cold outside. When we got there he turned to me and said softly, "It is hard, isn't it, to concentrate for so long to paint?' I nodded and then he said as he got out of the car, "You are close to this, aren't you? You know that?"

"Close to being able to concentrate you mean?" I said.

"Yes, you can still the mind. I can see that."

And I nodded adding, "But I want, need, to do so much more."

He smiled then and said, "Keep your mind pure and mindful and it will come. Do not lose faith. Do not become impatient. Let go."

"How shall I know?" I asked.

"You will know. One always knows," he said. Then he smiled, nodded his head and walked away.

He went away into the village and the rain and I never saw him again. I could not keep from laughing all the way back to Taba.

In Thailand it is said of monks that the holier they become the more love they exude. This surely was a very holy man. ❀

Erythrina arborescens Roxb.

Family

The children of Bhutan are just like children everywhere, full of life and motion, curiosity, shyness, smiles, tears and noise. They grow up in the extended family where the word *brother* could also mean first cousin, second cousin, or even close friend. *Uncle* is an affectionate term applied to people in various circumstances. *Father* could be anyone who looks after someone younger, and *mother* could be anyone who nurtures others.

Naming children in Bhutan is done by the monks. You take your child to them, they look for auspicious signs related to the calendar, the day of birth and other events related to the child, and then give it a name which usually sticks for life. Family names are not so important. Many people do not have a second, or family, name at all. This may result in some confusion for foreigners who find it hard to distinguish among two or three Ugyens or Rinchens or Pemas in the same office. At times it leads to foreigners calling someone "Gedu Rai" or "Taba Rai," adding a place to the name. Many names have religious connotations, such as Sangay or Dorji. Few names have any reference to the land, even though the people themselves are so closely tied to it.

One young fellow came to Thimphu from eastern Bhutan to work. If he had stayed at home he would have had small chance of finding paying work. He grew tired of tending the crops, protecting them from wild animals. He used to have to build a scaffold on which he slept at the edge of the field. He gathered stones in the evening so when monkeys and wild boars came to eat the corn or the potatoes, he had something to throw at them, and at the sun bears which came to eat apples and other fruit. He felt safer with the stones close at hand. It didn't give him much rest, though, and it didn't satisfy his desire for change. He felt a need to help his mother. His father had died some years before.

So he travelled to Dechhenchholing in the northwestern part of Bhutan, where he knew that a sister of his mother lived. His uncle was a royal bodyguard. The house was small and he had to share the space for sleeping with a growing, young family. Food was always difficult to find, especially when family and visitors came.

"My uncle is so kind," Rinchen used to say. "He gives me everything I need: food, shelter, clothes and shoes and pocket money." He did not tell anyone, however, that he freely gave his uncle his entire pay cheque every month and that his uncle saw this as natural and right. Rinchen did not think that he should keep anything for himself. He himself had very few needs and no concept of gathering anything for himself when other members of the family had needs too. His salary was no more private for him than his uncle's salary from the king was private for his uncle.

There were lean times for this growing family, but never once did Rinchen complain except to say that he felt badly that there was nothing he could send home to his mother in the east. He had come out west to earn money and here he was able only to sustain himself. But there was little thought for the future. He seemed so completely satisfied, maybe because he knew that he was loved and looked after. He may have been nineteen years old at the time.

Michelia doltsopa DC.

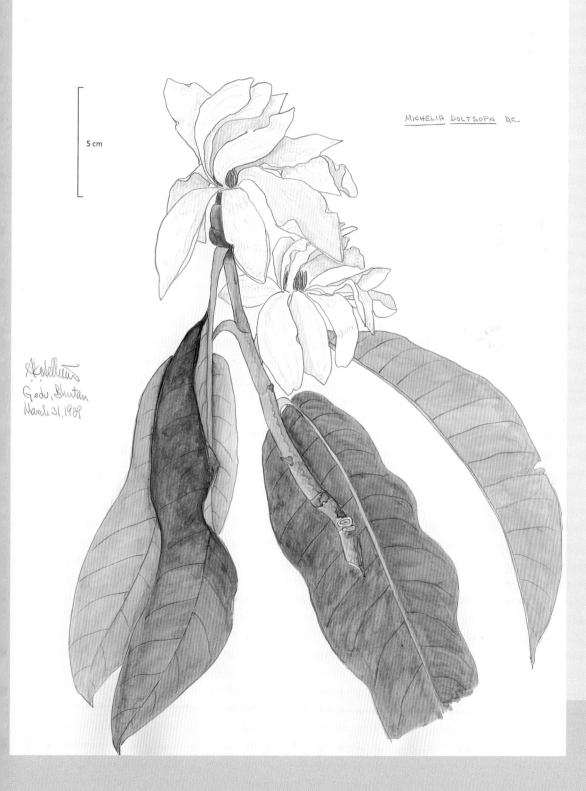

5 cm

MICHELIA DOLTSOPA D.C.

Gedu, Bhutan
March 31, 1989

When I gave him empty bottles to sell to get some money for his own use, he turned around and gave gifts to me because I had given him the bottles to sell. When he caught fish with hooks I gave him, he gave me the fish.

The concept of self is not well-developed in Bhutan because it goes against the Buddhist faith, where no one should stand out above anyone else. In fact, the Buddhist faith stresses the need to accept that there is no ego as we know it, and that everything is related with everything else, man or beast or plant. There is therefore no personal need which is greater than the need of one's neighbour or the needs of a suffering animal, insect or plant. We are all one and we all look after each other. That was how Rinchen could feel so cared for and be so free.

It is possible in Bhutan to marry many women, but they should all be from the same family. They should be sisters. But it is most common to marry only one woman. There are some men who are too poor to have a wife. They cannot support her alone. It is therefore also possible for two men to marry one woman. Generally speaking, a man and a woman live together if they like each other, and they do not bother so much with formalities or marriage in a Western sense. Foreigners are constantly surprised by the sudden relationships which form and they are equally surprised at how easily relationships are dissolved.

I did not find unwanted children or children who were uncared for, however, except in very unusual circumstances.

In fact the minimal awareness of the concept of "mine" and "yours" in Bhutan could lead to sharing which in a Western sense could create problems. Because things are not possessions but items to be used, what does it matter if the spoon is yours or mine?

This belief can certainly lead to problems in times of need and, as far as I could understand, did lead to dangers of mismanagement of natural resources. The beautiful magnolia tree *Michelia doltsopa*, for example, was becoming rare by the end of the 1980s because of over-harvesting for house building. The wood has a rich chocolate-brown colour. The same applies to the holy tree *Tsenden, Cupressus himalaica*, which is highly prized for building the inner temples of the *dzongs* because of its aromatic and very durable wood. ❅

The concept of self is not well developed in Bhutan because it goes against the Buddhist faith, where no one should stand out above anyone else.

5 cm

DAPHNE BHOLUA Buch.-Ham.
ex D.Don
var. GLACIALIS
(W.W.Smith & Cave)
Burtt

A.K.Hellum
March 25, 1990
Dorch La, Bhutan

The poisonous Daphne

Daphne (Daphne bholua) plants are poisonous when eaten. Norwegian legend says an arrow fashioned from its wood was used to kill Baldr, the son of Odin, the good god of the Vikings. In Bhutan, the inner bark of this plant is used for making brown, unbleached paper. This strong and decorative paper is made locally in many communities.

This bush flowers in March in the Dochu *La* pass in western Bhutan, and the air may be filled with such a strong aroma that it is almost sickening if you stay around for long. I found *Daphne* everywhere in the forests, from Gedu in the south to Thimphu in the north, and from Haa in the west to Tashigang in the east. There are several species native to Bhutan. Their fruits may be black or red, and their flowers white, creamy and pink, or even magenta. I could always tell a daphne bush by trying to break off a twig: you need a knife to cut it off, because the bast fibres of the inner bark are too tough to be torn. ✳

Daphne bholua Buch.-Ham. ex D. Don

5 cm

Aleotum
Gidakom Valley,
Bhutan
April 3, 1989.

RHODODENDRON

- species undescribed
- glaucous lower leaf
  surfaces, hairless
- probably ARBOREU
                    Smith

paint me a flower

This is the most common rhododendron (Rhododendron arboreum arboreum) in Bhutan of more than fifty different species. It can be found from valley bottoms to nearly 3,200 m above sea level. It flowers in late March and all through April. Girls pick the flowers and wear them in their hair to celebrate their youth, and the springtime.

One time, when painting in the Gidakom valley just west of the Thimphu valley, a small girl, maybe ten years old, came to me as I settled to paint a primula flower.

"Come," she said holding out her hand to me. "Come, see." She was so eager to show me something I gathered up my things and followed. We scrambled up a steep slope under blue pine, through some rose brambles and bushes of *Daphne* which I had come to paint too. She was so nimble and quick it was hard to keep up with her. Her *kira* flapped against her bare legs as she walked and climbed in her bare feet. Her hair was in disarray, and her eyes were smiling so beautifully back at me as she made sure I really was following.

As abruptly as she had entered my world she stopped and pointed. "There," she said and pointed to a small rhododendron bush just coming into flower. It was the first one that year. The buds were just bursting open, and red flowers poured from behind brown bud scales. She ran to the bush and tore off a branch and gave it to me. Then she stood still waiting for me to do the right thing. I said, "Thank you," but that didn't seem to do the trick. There was more to be done. I smelled the flower, which made her laugh because she knew that rhododendron flowers do not have a scent.

Then slowly I sat down in the grass and crossed my legs, took out my pad and pencil and started to draw the branch and flowers that she had given me. She sat down beside me. This was what she wanted, that I paint her flower. Slowly the drawing took shape and all the while she sat silently watching. She would lean forward now and then to get a closer look and every time I looked up at her, her eyes shone and her smile spread from ear to ear. She was so very pretty.

We sat side by side like this for more than two hours before the painting was finished. She had picked up every tube of paint to muse over the bright colours and she put each one down again carefully when finished. She had laughed when I poured water into the dish for mixing the paints. She had dipped her index finger into one colour to see if it also coloured her skin, spreading the colour with her other index finger as if painting herself.

May 4, 1990

5 cm

- Corollas deep crimson spotted with black dots in throat in bud
- small nectar sacks
- calyx lobes barely 1½mm long
- bright yellow petioles distinctive
- 10± flowers/head
- flowers pink to rose when unfolding.

RHODODENDRON ARBOREUM Smi
var. ROSEUM Lindl

A K Hellum
March 30, 1990
Above Taba, Bhutan

≫ *Rhododendron arboreum arboreum* Smith
≫ *Rhododendron arboreum* Smith *roseum* Lindley

When the job was done she stood up and looked at the picture for a long time, looking from the twig to the painting and back again. Then she smiled at me saying: "My plant?" And of course I gave her the painting. Then in her beautifully graceful way she ran off between the trees towards home and the slapping of the *kira* against her legs could be heard long after she disappeared from sight. She stopped on a small knoll, and turned just before disappearing altogether, and waved to me. Then she was gone.

I picked another rhododendron twig and sat down to draw and paint a second picture for myself. After that rhododendron there were daphnes to paint, and I forgot all about the primula. That had to wait for another time. Both *R. arboreum* var. *arboreum* and *R. arboreum* var. *roseum* grow in the Thimphu and Gidakom valleys. The former has deep red to crimson petals, while *roseum* has pink to rose petals with black-spotted throats on their corollas and small nectary sacs. The calyx lobes of the latter variety are barely 1 mm long. The petioles of its leaves are bright yellow and both *arboreum* and *roseum* have flower heads of ten or more flowers. ❋

The sap of euphorbias

To the Tibetans, Bhutan is the Land of Medicinal Herbs to the South, or *Lho Jong Men Jong*. To the Bhutanese it is *Druk Yul*, the Land of the Peaceful Dragon. To Western people it is Bhutan, or where the Bhutia people live.

Every plant used for its medicinal value in Bhutan has a local name, often Tibetan, which is hard to pronounce but still harder to remember for someone from the West. But to the Bhutanese the descriptive name helps one remember its healing value. Without *Dzongkha*, this information was inaccessible to me.

The root of *Euphorbia griffithii* produces a white sap that removes warts and cures abdominal problems, but the local name, *Thar-nu*, means nothing to an English speaker. I never found out what it means in Dzongkha. The sap is also used to remove hair and to induce vomiting. The sap of some species is corrosive to the skin, and some species produce sap that is used in rubber manufacture. I painted this particular specimen when it flowered near Dechhenchholing in late April, 1989. Because euphorbia is not eaten by cattle, I found it everywhere in the Thimphu valley. ❋

Bhutan is the Land of Medicinal Herbs
to the South

🌿 *Euphorbia griffithii* Hook.

EUPHORBIA
GRIFFITHII
Hook.

5 cm

Astellum
April 22, 1989
Taba, Bhutan

MAGNOLIA CAMPBELLII Hook.f. & Thoms.

DochuLa, Bhutan
April 28, 1990.

5 cm

Birds in a tree

The mountain passes in Bhutan were my favourite places to paint. Here I could spend whole days without running out of different species to record. Plants in the high passes flowered later than did the same species lower down. As a result I could catch some species that had already stopped flowering lower down.

But the mountains run mostly north and south, from the Tibetan ramparts to the steaming lowlands of India. There is one main highway which runs all the way from Haa in the north-west to Tashigang in the east of Bhutan, and this road crosses many high passes, some as low as 3,000 m, but others nearly 4,000 m high. I had to take out and clean the air filter from my rented car to be able to drive over some of these passes, because air filters were hard to come by in Bhutan and the filter in my car was old and very dirty.

The higher the passes, the more windswept they were, and the more inhospitable they became. It was the desolation in these places which appealed to me. It was here that I felt closest to Buddha's teachings. In spring, therefore, and before the rains of summer came, I travelled high up to paint.

Magnolia campbellii Hook. f. & Thomson

One of my favourite trees grows in the Dochu *La*. It is the *Magnolia campbellii*. In the Dochu *La* they grow among rhododendrons and daphnes and old hemlock trees, and they held me spellbound with their beauty. The flowers of *Daphne* grew in such profusion here that I felt at times heady with their scent.

The Bhutanese erect their prayer flags in these mountain passes to hinder bad spirits from crossing from one valley into the next. Here in the Dochu *La* I found prayer flags snapping their prayers to the heavens and to the spirits that watch over us.

Do means rock, *chu* means water, and *la* means pass. Dochu *La* is "the pass of rock and water." It is also a place where I could almost always find the wind sweeping the land. It moaned and whispered, tore at flags and ripped old ones from their poles. Sometimes it felt as if the gods were angry, and as if humans were struggling to communicate supplication to them.

The Dochu *La* is only about forty minutes by car from Thimphu. I could get up there quickly. It was just into the Wangdiphudrang valley to the east that the magnolias grew. I went there in late March and early April to see their flowers. Their black, bare trunks stand leafless and gnarled against the shifting skies, and the large and lax, white flowers looked like myriad white birds come to sit, or just taking off in flight. The trees brought promise of spring and the return to warmth for me. I would lie down on the ground under them and watch the sky with its drifting clouds above.

It is also here that *Piptanthus nepalensis* grows and flowers in April. It is planted in many parts of the world as an ornamental, but in the Dochu *La* it grows in dense thickets, its yellow pea-blossoms smiling at you from everywhere. This is a nitrogen fixer for the soil and is valuable for maintaining some soil fertility in what otherwise are cold and difficult places. ✳

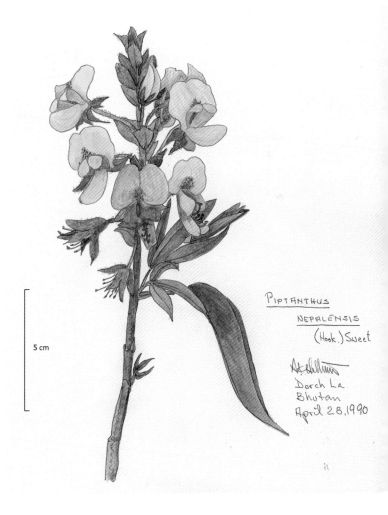

PIPTANTHUS
NEPALENSIS
(Hook.) Sweet

Dorch La
Bhutan
April 28, 1990

5 cm

🌸 *Piptanthus nepalensis* (Hook.) D. Don

5 cm

RHODODENDRON
FALCONERI Hook. f.

A.K. Hellum
Dochu La, Bhutan
April 29, 1990.

Personal identity

The Bhutanese are a mountain people who have lived in isolation and seclusion for centuries. Very few outsiders ever come in; very few Bhutanese ever leave. Mountain people are known worldwide to be strong and independent of body, and proud of mind. They love things as they are. The few tourists who are allowed into Bhutan are chaperoned very carefully. And foreign workers number only in the hundreds, working on aid programs and programs of cooperation. Itinerant people are not welcomed into Bhutan, and the marijuana which grows wild here is left for pig feed as it has been for centuries. Local people say marijuana makes the pigs sleepy so that they sit down a lot and grow fatter sooner.

The Bhutanese mind is not dependent on drugs to have visions. The country is so beautiful and so peaceful there are visions everywhere. The land still provides for most necessities of life, such as rice and potatoes, and all manner of delicious vegetables, fruit, and meat for those who eat it. Trout are plentiful in the rivers. Building materials and fuel wood can still be obtained with ease from the forests. The forests are still relatively untouched, at least in comparison with neighbouring Nepal. The land is extremely rugged, and the people seem healthy and very physically fit. Most of them rely on nature for fuel, mushrooms, berries and game, and they go to the forest to get them.

Women collect oak leaves in spring and carry them on their backs to fertilize their paddy-fields. Cattle graze the forests, and herders keep scrambling up and down slopes with their animals. People are found walking everywhere, and climbing 500 m up and coming 500 m down with heavy bundles of fuel wood on the back is a common event at least once a week for someone in most families.

The pride of the people finds expression in so many ways: in a fierce loyalty to their king and what he stands for, in a staunch belief in Bhutanese things and ways, in a love of Bhutanese dance, song and verbal banter, and in great prowess in archery, to name only a few. Because Bhutanese people have never been overrun by other peoples, they take it for granted that foreigners will respect local customs and ways.

When a Bhutanese person gives you something of herself or himself, it is a sign of respect for you, and you are expected to return it or at least to understand this gesture. Foreigners often misunderstand this, and thus offend without meaning to do so. One example of such giving came one Sunday morning, while I was eating breakfast in a hotel in Thimphu. I had taken my place at a vacant table and was just unfolding the paper napkin when I noticed a red, wet stain along one margin. "What is this red colour on the edge of the napkin?" I asked.

"Blood," said the waiter. "My blood." His face was raised high, he obviously spoke with pride. He had shared his blood with me.

"Oh," I said.

At other times Bhutanese people must put up with the ineptitudes of the foreigner. They do so with grace, but sometimes there is an incredulous look on their faces as if they want to say, "Can't you even do that?" Nowhere else is this more evident than in archery matches. The Bhutanese are remarkably good archers, hitting targets that are so small you can hardly see them. But most of the time they patiently put up with the problems foreigners have in coping with everyday little things, such as lack of electric power, lack of water, too many house flies, and the like.

One morning in the same hotel where the waiter shared his blood, the place was infested with flies that walked all over my food. The flies this morning were very persistent. "Have you got a swatter?" I asked. But the young waiter did not understand that word. So I explained by gesticulating and he understood quickly. He handed over a table napkin, a cloth one this time, and said casually, "Try this."

When I had swatted and missed a number of times with him looking on smiling, he asked for the napkin, took stoic aim at two flies just by the full coffee cup and darted into action killing both of them. He didn't as much as touch the saucer or the coffee. "There," he said and handed back the napkin with both hands. This ceremony of giving with both hands made the whole affair more formal, and I dropped all subsequent attempt to swat flies for fear of making too much out of a serious business. I ate quickly.

It is important to understand that to kill any living thing, even a house fly, is repugnant to a devout Buddhist. What the waiter had done was really above and beyond the call of duty. He had done his best to make a visitor feel comfortable but at his own discomfiture. As the waiter focused his attention on the two flies on the table, before striking and killing them, he had concentrated all his being on this one action. The fact that he had killed both flies with one blow and had not spilled coffee was, to me, an example of mindfulness at work. It was an example of the extraordinary power some Bhutanese have to concentrate their minds on certain things at a moment's notice. It comes from meditative strength and from centredness. The same waiter demonstrated this skill at several other times when work pressures in the restaurant were intense, such as when customers were complaining of slow service or wanting his attention when he was already more than busy. He never lost his calm but attended to one thing at a time, and in doing so was very efficient and pleasant to deal with.

After one of these times, when staying in the hotel, I packed up my painting materials and drove off to paint in the Dochu *La*. It was the end of April, and I wanted to catch the sulphur-yellow and green *Rhododendron falconeri*. It is a small tree here and when I found it, its long, large leaves were hanging down characteristically from a large inflorescence with about ten flowers. Its stem was hairy with dense brown pubescence, and its flowers were just coming into bloom. ✳

Clematis montana DC.

5 cm

CLEMATIS MONTANA DC.

Aquilium
Punakha trail
   near Dechhenchholing, Bhutan.
May 5, 1990.

*The Punakha
   is an old trail...
it used to be the trail
   that the monks
walked in fall and
   spring.*

Going to market

The common clematis in Bhutan, *Clematis montana*, scrambles over other vegetation reaching many meters from its roots to its flowering tips. It is called "Virgin's bower plant." It makes for small private hiding places under its hanging branches, leaves and flowers.

The plant flowered in early May in 1990 along the Punakha trail from Dechhenchholing, and past the village of Kabjisa. A man was wearing a flowering twig behind his right ear as he walked along the trail, and the children with him laughed and joked and tried to pull it off. They stopped when they saw me, peered over my work and pointed to the man to come closer to see the flower in my painting. But he was not interested because he was carrying a heavy sack of root vegetables to market. And the children, not wanting to be left behind, scampered after him down the trail. They were on their way to the Thimphu market, the big event of the week. And there was money to be made for next week's staples. The sack bent the man as he walked, and Thimphu was maybe seven kilometers away. And how far had he walked already? I was thinking he might catch a jeep taxi from Dechhenchholing. That would mean he would have only two more kilometers to walk. It seemed like he could use some rest. But he walked on, not noticing. The load looked very heavy, but men who cannot afford horses must carry their own burdens to market on their backs each week, as the crops mature.

The Punakha trail goes over the mountains from Thimphu to Punakha. This is an old trail, described over two hundred years ago by Collister, which used to be the trail that the monks walked in fall and spring. It still looks very well travelled. 🌸

A.K.Hellum
May 5, 1990
Changaphug valley
near treeline
Bhutan

RHODODENDRON CAMPANULATUM D. Don

subsp. AERUGINOSUM
(Hook. f.) Chamberlain

5 cm

Mother Nature's garden

There is a small hill above the road at the top of the Changaphug valley where this rhododendron *(R. campanulatum)* grows. It is a place above the fir forest where only patches of *Rhododendron* alternate with patches of *Piptanthus* in full yellow bloom, and where the grasses are chewed to the ground by yaks. Here, on warm and windy spring days when the snows are melting and the ground is soggy under foot with run-off water, the rhododendron buds and their pale purple petals gather colour from the sun. This place is a garden more perfect than any garden made by humans. Gently, ever so cautiously, life returns to this place above the tree-line, maybe 3,900 m above sea level. Life is so cautious at first, so hesitant about emerging. It ponders what surprises might lie ahead. But once the process has started it moves fast, very fast. Within days everything is in bloom and the colours are breathtaking.

These alpine places are cared for in a way only Mother Nature could. This caring stood in bold contrast to the logged area nearby where the firs had all been removed.

The fir trees had died. They died not only here but in many high places in Bhutan and I could not say for certain why. Was it because the fogs were absent here for long enough that the firs died from drought? Was it some disease that killed them? Was it an insect no one had found yet? But the fir forest was old, very old, and would have needed to renew itself anyway. Maybe this mass dying was part of the natural cycle of things. But the logging had left a barren and unsightly hillside in stark contrast to the beautiful place where I sat and painted in the sharp sunshine.

When May comes to the Thimphu valley all manner of rhododendrons burst forth into bloom: large ones, and showy ones, and small and timid ones like *Rhododendron virgatum*. It grows along the road between Thimphu and Taba and if you do not look carefully, you could miss it altogether. Its purple petals hardly poke their heads above the grass. When I painted this specimen, I sat beside a small creek where people came to collect water in buckets and cattle grazed all around me.

🌿 *Rhododendron campanulatum* D. Don subsp. *aeruginosum* (Hook. f.) Chamb.

🌿 *Rhododendron virgatum* Hook. f.

5 cm

RHODODENDRON KESANGIAE Long a finch forth.

N.K.Hellum
Mai 13, 1990
Dochu La, Bhutan

One time in mid-May, I returned to the Dochu *La* to paint another rhododendron. I had come looking for a recently described species called *Rhododendron kesangiae*. It is a very large, bushy plant with a huge inflorescence at the tips of the shoots with well over twenty flowers. It took me a whole day to paint this one, and afterwards I went to bed and slept until the next morning. There were so many rhododendrons to paint at this time of year that I felt like a child in a candy store with only two cents to my name. ❊

The road workers

A rhododendron (*Rhododendron cinnabarinum xanthocodon*) of the higher places grows at well above 3,500 m in several of the passes along the roads in Bhutan. It is not common in Chele *La* at about 4,000 m, but its flowers are so sulphury yellow the bush can be spotted a long way off. So, if you go to the Chele *La* in May you should see this unusual rhododendron. It is unusual because of its funnel-shaped flowers with fused petals. And the tubes open only at their tips, spreading yellow-greenish petals so that the stamens and style protrude.

It was too cold and wet to sit outside and paint on this day in late May. So I sat in the car concentrating away everything around me. It was not until the car started to rock that I noticed two road workers, dark-faced young men staring in through the window at my drawing, their noses squashed against the window, their bodies resting against the door. A large circle of condensation had formed on the glass around each nose. Their eyes twinkled. Their closeness startled me.

These two men were part of a much larger group of road workers now working their way in groups across the pass into the Haa valley and home. It was getting on for four-o'clock pick-up, and I am sure they were hungry and tired. Their shovels and picks were resting on the ground, their hands gripping the handles loosely. They looked cold in their tattered clothes and rubber footwear, and their caps were pulled down over their ears. But when I smiled at them they smiled back and their gleaming white teeth fairly shone.

❧ *Rhododendron kesangiae* Long & Rush.

Road workers often visited me in my concentration. Their poverty always touched me. These workers were aliens, speaking only Nepali and Hindi, and I spoke neither language. They were very shy people who did not want their pictures taken, nor did they really accept my presence on this, "their" piece of road. I had seen them earlier when driving up to the pass as they sat by their small fires, shielded by umbrellas against the penetrating cold. It had been raining and their fires were smoky, not clean, and they smelled of smoke as they stood by the car.

In Bhutan, gravel for the roads is crushed by hand, and tar is melted over smoking wood fires before it is mixed with the gravel and used to surface the road. The women do most of the crushing, with a hammer and a small ring of metal held by a handle to contain the stones as they are smashed. The men cut the wood, mostly from the forest floor or from standing dead trees. They roll this wood down hill and truck it to their places of tar smoke and wood heat. They melt the tar on ovens made from tar drums covered with gravel crushed by the women and fuelled

with the wood. On top of these they put vats of tar to heat. They mix the tar with the gravel, and then men wheel the mix with wheelbarrows to the parts of the road to be repaired. Because the roads are all handmade, they are only as wide as absolutely necessary. They twist and turn their way across the rough terrain that is Bhutan.

Roads built any other way would probably not last one season, as a monk had told me long before. He had told me that the mountains are unstable in Bhutan and weather is indiscriminate in its harshness during monsoon rains, and in winter with snows and ice. The roads follow the paths of least resistance and that is how it must be. Somehow, because the roads have been built by hand, this way, they fit into the countryside, and they seem so natural and unobtrusive. ❃

5 cm

Rhododendron cinnabarinum Hook f.
subspecies XANTHOCODON
(Hutch.) Cullen

At Atellium
Chele La, Bhutan, 4000m
May 20, 1990.

❧ *Rhododendron cinnabarinum* subsp. *xanthocodon* (Hutch.) Cullen

A high-altitude rhododendron.

The Changaphug valley is narrow, and the road up to the fir logging is vulnerable to washouts during the summers. It is rough passage to get up, and often the road is barred by logging trucks. Waiting until they are loaded with wood can take a long time. But one mid-May morning, I was able to get to the top without trouble to paint yet another flowering bush, *Rhododendron campylocarpum*. This species is common at higher altitudes, around timber-line, and its flowers come and go very quickly in spring. They seem to last only a few days. The flower heads are composed of about half a dozen flowers in pale to darker purple. As in most rhododendrons, the styles protrude beyond the petals and the brown-tipped stamens cluster just below the rim of the petals. The stamens are commonly ten in number, the leaves are dark green on the upper side and much paler, almost white, below. ✳

Flies, flies and more flies

This raspberry (Rubus biflorus) has yellow-orange fruits that are very sweet and succulent. Local people collect them and eat them so enthusiastically that it is hard to find an untouched bush anywhere. In winter the plant is bare of leaves, and the stems have a whitish bloom on them so they can be identified everywhere you go. The plant is very common. But in summer, when the stems grow in girth, the white bloom is much less visible and the other greenery around hides the plant, which tends to scramble over other vegetation. The name *biflorus* means that the flowers always occur in pairs.

One morning in mid-May 1989, I could not stand waiting any longer for warm weather to come. I bundled up my books on plant identification with some oranges and water and two chocolate bars, packed all the paints and papers I would need for a full day outside, and put on an extra sweater and long underwear to keep me warm while sitting still for hours. I pulled a wool cap over my ears and set out. I walked along the road from Taba towards Dechhenchholing. But I walked farther towards Begana before finding this raspberry. Then I sat down in the shrubbery.

This painting was my second try. The first was totally destroyed by the flies that came in droves as the nearby cattle grazed around me. Cattle and flies go together. The flies walked all over the paints and then landed on the painting, leaving tracks all around.

🪶 *Rhododendron campylocarpum* Hook. f.

5 cm

RHODODENDRON
CAMPYLOCARPUM
Hook. f.

A.E.Hellum
May 19, 1990.
Changaphug Valley, Bhutan.

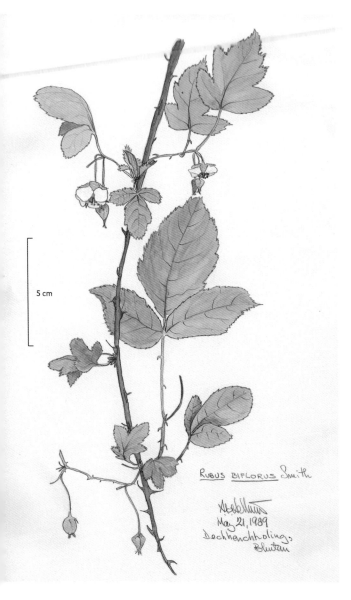

5 cm

RUBUS BIFLORUS Smith

May 21, 1989
Dechhenchholing,
Bhutan

This led me to painting flies rather than paper. Blue flies, red flies, yellow flies and green flies soon buzzed around everywhere. They didn't seem to mind at all, nor did the paint interfere with their flying. And the drawing started to look more like a paint-by-numbers picture than a flower after a while. Not only footprints from flies, but dabs of paint where I missed flies, adorned the paper. It was a blessing for me that no one came around that day to see what I was up to. A good Buddhist would not have understood the frustration at all.

When I got home to my apartment that afternoon, intending to redraw and repaint this plant, I noticed that my face was spotty with paint too. No wonder people along the road had looked at me strangely as I walked home. ✳

Rubus biflorus Buch.-Ham. ex Sm.

When the monsoon season comes,
one could get caught away from home for long periods
unless one was willing to walk home over passes,
following trails hundreds of years old.

Summer

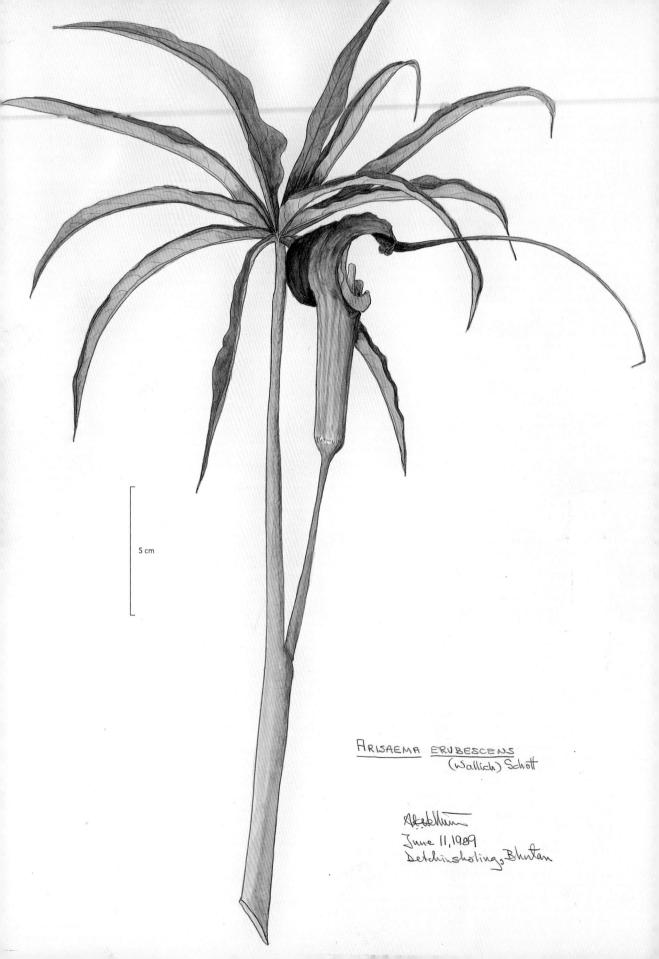

5 cm

ARISAEMA ERUBESCENS
(Wallich) Schott

June 11, 1989
Detchinsholing, Bhutan

Summer

SUMMER COMES GRADUALLY TO THE THIMPHU VALLEY, and you don't know when to say, "This is summer." Summer is usually synonymous with monsoon rains, when everything grows fast and the paddy fields look their emerald best. Summer was the time when travelling in and out of Bhutan by air was problematic because of cloud, and when road travel became a problem because of landslides. One could get caught away from home for long periods unless one was willing to walk home over passes, following trails hundreds of years old.

One consultant working in Tashigang in the East had to walk all the way to Thimphu. It took him weeks, and he had to leave all his belongings behind. I was told he walked his way through two pairs of runners and spent weeks visiting places of great isolation in the process. The road from Thimphu to Phuntsholing on the Indian border to the south was regularly closed because of slides that could take days to clear. It was therefore best to limit travel during summer and always to carry extra cash in one's pocket to manage times of enforced delay. When the road was closed, supplies of gasoline and kerosene ran short in the capital, and people lined up for their quotas. Even tropical fruits, such as bananas, would be in short supply during market days. ✳

🌿 *Arisaema erubescens* (Wall.) Schott

Can't you see it's purple?

Snake plant, or Jack-in-the-pulpit (*Arisaema erubescens*), is common in the Thimphu valley. It flowers in late May and into June and its seeds ripen in October, when the entire plant collapses and the spadix with the bright orange and red seeds falls down, dangling upside down from some other plant as if it were a part of it.

So I painted closer to home during these months, from June to September. While I was painting this plant a small boy came to watch. He carried on a string of conversations with every passer-by on the trail to Dechhenphug, where the old armouries of Thimphu are hidden up a side valley from Dechhenchholing. "It is a useless plant," he said to me in good English. "We do not eat it, cattle leave it alone and it is not poisonous." Would it have been useful if it had been poisonous? He also thought the colour dull and uninteresting. When I had applied the green background to the flower he commented that I had chosen the wrong colour. "Can't you see it is purple?" he said. I waited patiently until he had finished and then applied the purple over the green, as I had intended to do in the first place. "That's better," he said, surveying the work. And then he started to attract passers-by, advertising what I was doing. "You want to see this painting?" he would say, accosting someone on the trail. No, most were just on their way home on this late afternoon, so they had no time. But some came to see and to comment. "You see the purple colour there," he would say, pointing to the flower he had just criticized me for. "That is almost what it looks like on this plant," as he held up a greenish specimen he had found.

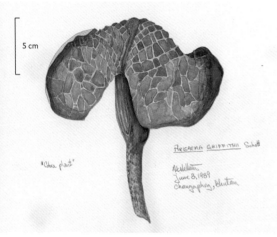

5 cm

ARISAEMA GRIFFITHII Schott

Aksldellum
June 3, 1989
Changaphug, Bhutan

"Cobra plant"

It is amazing how well Bhutanese children are taught English in the army school at Dechhenchholing, and this boy obviously showed off his skill even to those who understood only Dzongkha and who shook their heads and smiled at his antics.

There is another species of the genus *Arisaema* that I found now and then in the Changaphug valley behind Thimphu to the east. It looks like a woman's hat flopped on the head without care. It is soft and pulpy, purple to black. It is the species *Arisaema griffithii*. This plant is so rare that I never saw it in fruit, only this dilapidated hat-shape. The insects that come to pollinate this plant have to crawl up under the hat, where many die when they fall into the throat of the plant and drown in juices at its base. It is an insectivorous genus. ✳

*It looks like a woman's hat flopped
on the head without care.*

๛ *Arisaema griffithii* Schott
๛ *Arisaema erubescens* (Wall.) Schott

infloresence
hanging upside
down from rose
bush once plant
wilted in fall.

5 cm

ARISAEMA ERUBESCENS
(Wallich) Schott

Asterellum
October 14, 1989
Dochu La, Bhutan

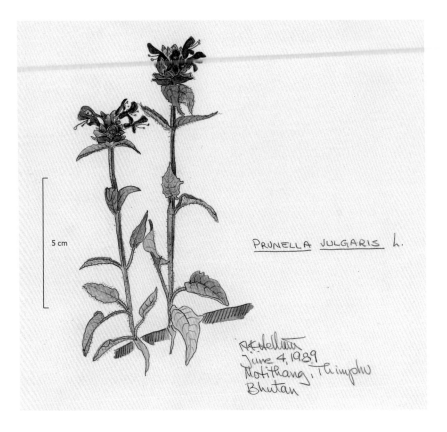

PRUNELLA VULGARIS L.

5 cm

A.K. Nellian
June 4, 1989
Motithang, Thimphu
Bhutan

Methoo

Methoo (Prunella vulgaris) is a common member of the mint family that grows well in Europe, as it does in the Himalayas and even in North America. These plants grew by the road to upper Thimphu, Mutigthang, in early June 1989. Their brown and bristly seed heads in fall are as handsome as the springtime flowers.

While concentrating on this painting, I was suddenly chased into the car by a rain squall, a harbinger of the monsoon rains of summer. Here I sat in silence working as a taxi came past and stopped to let out passengers. A large family poured forth from the tiny jeep. Among the members were two small boys who walked by my car banging it with a stick as they went. When they saw me sitting inside, they stopped suddenly and grew silent for a moment.

They came up to the partly open window and peered in. When their noses poked their way into the car I turned suddenly and said "BOO." They jumped back laughing wildly. Then they advanced again to have another look as I again concentrated on the painting. They had all sorts of comments to make, one to the other. But they spoke in Dzongkha which I could not understand.

Then a dirty hand inched its way into the car and a dirtier finger yet pointed to the flower. One voice said, raspingly, "*Methoo.*" This is the word for flower, one of the few I learned during my stay there. The other boy drew in a deep breath, sucking in a large drivel of snot, and said: "Uh-huh." But the snot came out again almost as soon as it had disappeared.

By this time I had lost all power of concentration. The talk, the snot and the noise of breathing in my ear, all contributed to the loss. I turned to them and smiled, and they withdrew a few paces to stare at me. Up until that point I had not really been a person to them because I had been sitting so still and working in spite of their presence. And once they saw I was really alive, they ran away up the hill, chasing each other and trying to catch up with their family.

Interruptions by children only deepen this tranquility and enrich life, making me feel part of a much larger community. ✳

Loading a truck

Seven men were loading a truck by hand with logs from the Chamena beetle-kill area above Taba where I sat to paint this windflower. Men always load trucks by hand in Bhutan because that is what they have always done. These logs had been taken down the mountain by cable and winch, paid for by the World Bank. The logs were dumped where they could be picked up and driven to sawmills in the Thimphu valley. The beetle, *Ips schmutzenhoferi*, has done a lot of damage to spruce in northwestern Bhutan. The theory is that the populations of this beetle were able to get started in fresh logging slash, and once that happened then live timber started to get infected everywhere. Infected trees brought on trouble for more healthy stands if the dead and dying trees were not felled and debarked quickly.

This windflower, *Anemone obtusiloba*, is a common plant in the Himalayas, growing in the Thimphu valley and flowering in early June. The windflowers we have in Alberta are tinged with red, mauve or crimson, but they are rarely bluish purple like this one. There are about 120 temperate-region species world-wide of this genus. It inhabits forest margins and small openings in the patchy blue pine forests above Taba. It has no special medicinal value that I know of. Small, growing in among other vegetation, it can easily be overlooked.

Only four men were actually loading the truck. One man shouted orders and then the three men grunted in response and unison as all four of them pushed the logs up ramps. The shouts and answers were so regular they sounded like music. There was no other sound up above Taba except calls from two crows, *choughs*, flying overhead. These had red bills and red legs, as I remember, and looked all dressed up. They called to each other as they soared on convection currents.

In between periods of concentration, I could raise my head to look out over the valley below. On a far hill stood prayer flags fluttering intensely in the afternoon sun and wind of unsettled weather. Behind them a dark mountainside rose, covered in scrub oak and pine. Where I sat it was dead calm and lightly overcast. Heavy clouds were moving in quickly overhead, however, telling of coming rain. Before I finished the painting, I was forced to flee for cover under a large spruce tree until the shower passed.

5 cm

ANEMONE OBTUSILOBA
D. Don

A.E.Hollins
Above Taba
Bhutan
June 3, 1989.

The squall did not stop the Bhutanese men from working. Before the weather cleared they were finished. Six of the men drove down the hill in the truck, three of them on top of the load of logs, the other three in the cab. The seventh man, who stayed under a makeshift cover, came over when the rain stopped and sat down, smoking a cigarette and eating some rice from his bamboo bowl. Then he lit a fire, boiled some water and offered me a cup of tea in the only cup he had. When I finished he had his drink. The kindness of the people in Bhutan is astounding to a Westerner like me who has been taught to mind his own business. But this man did not express any interest in what I was doing, he just wanted a rest and to have some company while he had his lunch, I guess.

The dogwood *Cornus capitata* grows in similar situations to the windflower, on exposed hillsides and in more-open sunny places. This plant is not very common in the Thimphu area. Its inflorescences have four large petaloid bracts of a cream colour that complements the yellow-green of the leaves. The wood is sometimes used for skewers and for bobbins. Its trunks rarely grow big enough for lumber, but the wood is suitable for furniture-making. ✳

No problem

I had much to learn about patience from the people of Bhutan. I could also learn a lot from them about the wisdom of not trying to anticipate the future. I was often so impatient, so dependent on support systems, so intense about getting the job done, that small and large impediments to progress became grating to me, and I made repetitive complaints to a people for whom time is definitely not money. I felt helpless about this sense of urgency for it rarely if ever led to any satisfaction. Bhutan should send ambassadors abroad to bring some sanity and relaxation to the frenzy of Western living.

I decided to grow a beard when the water heater failed once again. I stored water in buckets and pots for when the supply failed, as I knew it would. I even learned how to cook with a pressure cooker because water was in such short supply at times. I used a battery pack on my computer to give me a few minutes' grace to store information when the power failed. Voltage could at times exceed 300 V, and then drop again to well below 130 V, though it was supposed to be a steady 220. But I never learned to sit and wait for the photocopier to get fixed, because there were places in Thimphu where copying could be done, for a price. I went there and paid out of my own pocket instead of waiting for the repairman. He could take days to arrive from India.

One of my experiences of impatience, like so many in Bhutan, had to do with water, or the lack of it.

❧ Anemone obtusiloba D.Don

On my first morning in a hotel, there was no hot water. I turned the taps on, both hot and cold, to make sure that even if labels were switched I would find hot water if there was any. But there was only a sputtering of water from the hot line—a sputter, and then a long, drawn-out moan as water was sucked down the pipe away from my sink and to God knows where. Waiting did not seem to help. The moan ended and stillness filled the room.

I alerted the manager to the problem, and a plumber was called for. In the meantime, a waiter went up to the room to check things out. He came down saying there was ample water: wonderful, very hot water. Upon my returning to my room in a rush, his words were indeed verified. There was ample hot water, and, for me, silent embarrassment.

The next morning, there was a repeat performance: a sputter of water from the hot tap, followed by the low moan and then utter silence. I waited this time to see what would happen. But nothing seemed to happen, so I went down again to the front desk. "There is no hot water!" I said. Again the stolid waiter went up, only to find hot water pouring from the tap. He looked at me very quizzically this time as if to say, "What *is* your problem?" I returned to the room mortified, for there sure was hot water. It sounded like a waterfall as I approached.

The answer lay in one simple fact: when the tap was turned on, the water was indeed sucked out, but given about five minutes it came back and in full force. I had not waited long enough. The solution is to know when to wait and when to act.

Do not go to a Bhutanese with an anticipated problem, therefore. There really is no problem except in your head. Don't gather things today for the disaster or the need of tomorrow. It may never come. When it comes, then stay flexible enough to find a solution. There usually is one if you look again, carefully.

If it is a water problem, it might be a frog stuck in the water-line, which did happen where I lived, or sediment, or a piece of plastic covering the intake, which also happened when the headman of the village did not put the money my landlord had paid him into the general village fund. It could be almost anything. In time I was able to become a little more flexible and phlegmatic, but it wasn't easy.

In fact, people in the West pride themselves on anticipating future problems and forestalling them before they have a chance to happen. That is why our support systems function so well, and that is also why our solutions fail so miserably in much of Asia or Africa when they are introduced through outside aid. This is especially true after projects

38

CORNUS CAPITATA (Wall. in Roxb.)
(BENTHAMIDIA)

Atchollum
Helela, Bhutan
June 16, 1990.

5 cm

🌿 *Cornus capitata* (Wall.)

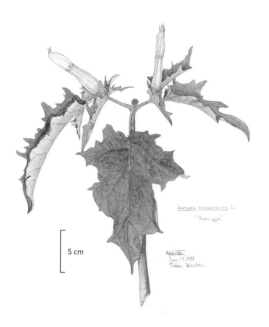

DATURA STRAMONIUM. L.
"Thorn apple"

5 cm

Addition
June 19, 1989
Talan, Bhutan.

end, when no one is left around to worry like we do. In Bhutan, there is no such thing as an anticipated breakdown. There either is a breakdown or there is none. To plan for a disaster which has not occurred is in the realm of paranoia, not reality.

I remember one day when the water supply to my apartment had failed yet another time, and I drove into Thimphu to buy breakfast at the Druk Hotel rather than worry about what was wrong. As I parked my car by the hotel, by some open ground, I heard a rattling sound as the wind blew around the corner of the hotel. I went to check and found a patch of thorn apples. The seed heads on these datura plants rattle in the wind.

Rattle, rattle, rattle and then quiet, and then more rattling. It sounded like tiny castanets, soft and high-pitched. But because the wind was gusty, there was no syncopation or rhythm to the sounds. It was as if they were trying to catch my attention, as if they were saying, "There are other matters which are more worthwhile than worrying about the water. Take a break and don't be tempted by anger."

I thought, then, about why the Bhutanese often ring bells. They do this to open up a way for their prayers. These datura pods were like bells of nature and I was being reminded of the need to be centred rather than dispersed in my mind. ✳

The disciple

One day, when I drove up to the Dochu La to paint, I was flagged down by a family standing by their car. If I was going to Wangdiphudrang, would I take this woman along? I told them I was only going to the Dochu *La*, some distance up the road. I agreed to take her there, even though I knew that if I had been her I would have waited farther down, because the pass is a cold place. She got in on the passenger side, and we spoke for a long time about religion. She was studying at Varanasi in India, preparing herself for monastic service. She had a sense of calmness about her that was so pronounced I could not stop admiring her and what she had mastered. She wondered why she seemed to get men to eat from her hand, and in response to my answer she expressed some amusement at the idea that she had some power over men's thoughts. I retorted by saying that she underestimated the power of her soothing calmness, which she said had come to her through being a disciple of the Dalai Lama of Tibet.

🌿 *Datura stramonium* L.

We reached the top of the pass, and I got out to paint this iris (*Iris clarkei*). She went berry-picking, because the roadside was covered with wild strawberries. While she waited for a lift on into the Wangdiphudrang valley, I painted for the next two hours.

We met again then after my concentration was exhausted. She had a handkerchief full of berries, and I had a line drawing for this iris. She stopped and looked at the drawing, making some comment regarding my powers of concentration. As we stood there looking into each other's lives a truck came belching up the hill towards us. She hurriedly divided the strawberries into two piles and gave me one half, which I put in my cap. I wanted to give her my drawing, but she was gone before I could offer her anything in return.

I have often thought back to that moment on the road with a sense of sadness because of that hurried parting. She gave me her address in Varanasi but I have lost it. I wonder now where she is and what level of awareness she has reached. She reminded me of the monk who was interested in my paintings. ❀

The operation

People in Bhutan like hospitals as little as people in the West do. Sick people commonly seek out traditional doctors and monks for help before going to the hospitals where they operate and use modern drugs. As a result people who go to hospital in Bhutan often go there and die, when they have become too sick to be healed. This has led to some people thinking that hospitals are places to die rather than places to get well.

It is not that traditional medicines fail so much as it is that people get really ill before they seek outside help. Sometimes the trail is hard or impossible to travel when you are sick. Sometimes the local *drungtso*, or traditional doctor, or the monk, is away. Sometimes the traditional medicines are not powerful enough to give cures as quickly as needed. And sometimes people use their own medicinal cures, passed down from mother to daughter with utmost faith in their healing power, in spite of people getting weaker. Sometimes the hope that an illness will go away if ignored fails to carry the day, and sometimes it is strong enough to heal.

Because the Bhutanese believe we all have our own karma to live out, people hesitate to interfere. What is ordained may not be alterable.

Even when people do seek modern medicine, they often fail to take the last step and have an operation because they are afraid of the unknown, and afraid that they might die in hospitals as they know others have before them.

No one likes falling ill, least of all where sufficient help often is so hard to find. And, as in so much of the Buddhist world, a long life is a blessing. It is visible proof of the fact that you have been a good human being and have avoided illness and death for so long. It gives you time to gain merits and time to increase your life's wisdom. Your chances of being reborn again as a human

❀ *Iris clarkei* Baker ex Hook. f.

5 cm

IRIS CLARKEI Baker ex.
Hook. f.

A.K.Hellum
Doroh La, Bhutan
June 23, 1990.

A small tree with stringy
silvery bark.

BUDDLEJA COLVILEI
Hook. f. & Thomas

5 cm

June 25, 1989
Dochu La, Bhutan

being, rather than as an animal, are increased. Animals cannot pray and cannot speed the process towards enlightenment. That is something only human beings can do. A long life also gives you more opportunity to gain understanding and approach enlightenment. Illness seems a sign that you've fallen off that path.

A mother was ill and needed an operation to remove a large growth. Rinchen, her son, said it had been impossible to convince her to have the stomach operation. It did not matter that there were days when her stomach pains overwhelmed her and she could not eat at all without throwing up. She could not eat her favourite chilis. Ever so slowly, she discovered those things which did not bring on pain when eaten and that she could keep down without vomiting. She stayed with these foods, accepting that much of her joy in eating had left her.

At times she was unable to work, and at other times she sent messages to her son in Thimphu to come to her as her days seemed numbered. He made the long journey through India to reach eastern Bhutan, and he stayed with her for about a month in 1990. When she got better he returned to his labourer's job in the capital, but he worried about her and about the fact that he had no siblings with whom to share his fears of losing her.

One day Rinchen announced that his mother was coming to Thimphu to have the operation, in spite of everything. He was delighted yet apprehensive.

During this period of waiting I went painting, again in the Dochu *La*. I had seen several new flowering plants up there in mid-June and I wanted to meditate on them. Rinchen's worries also affected me. What could I do for her when she came?

Along the road just below Hungtso on the way to Dochu *La*, I spied a *Buddleja* species, a member of a genus with about a hundred warm-temperate members. Its drooping, deep mauve to purple flowers are so attractive that many members of this genus are planted world-wide. Some have medicinal value, and some grow large enough to produce lumber, but this particular species was a bush where it grew.

I found the bush, sat down and concentrated on it. It felt to me as if the flowers of this plant were the blood from Rinchen's mother, because I was thinking of her. What would Rinchen's mother do? Would she have to be coerced into going to see the doctor once she got here? How sick was she really and how much understanding would she get if she did go to the hospital with all her worries and fears?

After painting the *Buddleja* species, I was still very unsettled of mind and drove to the pass where I knew that orchids were in bloom. Up there, I found a *Pleione* species I had seen before. It grew as an epiphyte on the gnarled oaks up there. It somehow looked both frail and robust growing just outside the little tea-house. The parts of the Scottish *Flora of Bhutan* which had been completed by 1989 did not cover the orchids, so I was unable to identify the plant to species level. Four hours passed while I completed this painting. I was so tired I slept in my car for a while until I woke from the cold. Then I drove home, feeling more at peace with things than in that morning's turmoil while waiting for Rinchen's mother.

Buddleja colvilei Hook. f. & Thoms.

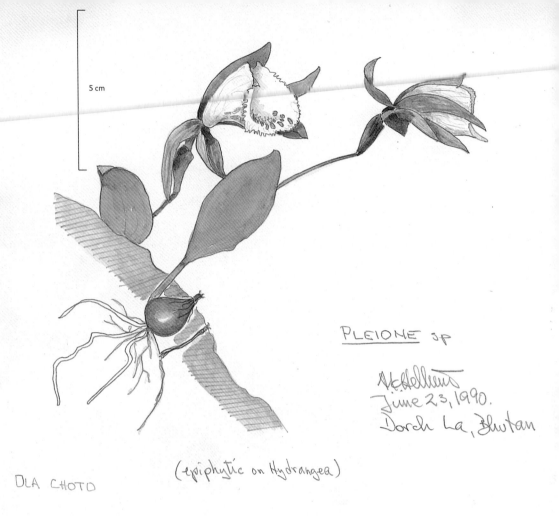

PLEIONE sp

McBellium
June 23, 1990.
Dorch La, Bhutan

(epiphytic on Hydrangea)

DLA CHOTO

Rinchen's mother came one spring day with her own father and with the man she had been living with since Rinchen's father died.

When the day for going to the hospital came—for she had agreed to see the doctor—she was nowhere to be found. She had gone visiting friends. We hunted high and low, asking everywhere if anyone had seen her, with her father and her companion. Finally, she emerged from a small hill settlement where Rinchen had gone to hunt for her. We were some distance outside of the capital, by Lungtenphu, on a hill overlooking the Wang _Chu_, which flows through Thimphu and south into India. The weather was warm and gentle and the sun was powerful and bright under the willows and poplars where we waited.

And when she arrived at the hospital the fear of the place silenced her. Even her son's careful prodding led to nothing. She had been immovable at the doctor's office, and equally silent when visiting the bed she had been assigned in Thimphu General Hospital. She had made up her mind not to have the operation after all. Because she spoke Shashop, the language of eastern Bhutan, Rinchen had to translate into Dzongkha for the doctor. There was considerable talk between mother and son, but very little was translated for the doctor or for the ears of others, nor did

Pleione sp. D. Don

Rinchen translate all that the doctor said to his mother, judging by his short communications. The air was filled with feelings and apprehensive gestures.

Finally a decision was reached. The woman rose from her seat, lifted her head, straightened her back and walked slowly out of the doctor's office. She was a proud woman, and independent, and she could not be persuaded by her son nor made to feel confident by the quiet and metered voice of the doctor.

It was about a month later that Rinchen announced that his mother was going back to Pemagatshel, a village near Tashigang, with her father and her companion. She visited family and friends, her father had taken Rinchen to Paro and Haa, and they had seen many exciting places together. But the time had come to get back home and attend to the crops they had planted before leaving on this expedition.

"Come and have a bowl of *tukpa* with me at Benez's restaurant before they leave," I suggested to Rinchen. He agreed, and within hours we were on our way to eat a meal together. While waiting for the traditional Bhutanese soup, several drinks were poured, and the other men drank Special Courier with me, while Rinchen's mother was convinced that apple juice would not hurt her stomach. Rinchen joined her. She had apparently never had apple juice from a bottle like that before. She was very cautious, and sipped the liquid at first. Her *tukpa* was prepared without chilis and without much chicken. It was best for her stomach that it be mostly pure broth, without even cabbage or carrots.

During this meal, the restaurant filled with customers arriving for lunch and, as usual, the noise level grew high, matching the merriment among the customers. In all this din, Rinchen said casually into my ear, "Mother went to hospital." After a stunned silence he said she went to the Traditional Medicine Hospital and had acupuncture fourteen days previously. "Show him," he said to his mother in Shashop. Without as much as a comment, she unhooked her silver *koma* clasps from her *kira*, lowered the *kira* top and lifted her yellow blouse up over her head exposing her bare chest. I gasped and looked down but found that no one around me thought this unusual. No one seemed to have noticed. She lowered her blouse just enough to see the look on my face. When she saw my embarrassment she lowered the blouse just enough to cover her breasts.

"There," Rinchen said, pointing a finger right into his mother's solar plexus. There small blood droplets, or spots, on the skin surface in a neat square pattern. "She is well now," Rinchen said proudly. "No more pain."

Rinchen did not remember having been told that the growth his mother had in her abdomen could not be cured by acupuncture at this late stage. He wanted to believe, as she did, that the growth was now waning and would soon disappear. But several months later he did admit that his mother was again ill in Pemagatshel, and his assuredness during that parting meal was now gone. His worries for her were back. ✳

Years later, I know Rinchen's mother is alive, so maybe the acupuncture really did work.

Thimphu?

Transportation in Bhutan is always in short supply. What vehicles there are, are regularly overloaded. Buses are crowded beyond belief, often with people hanging out windows everywhere when the weather permits. Trucks carry heavy loads with people scrambling everywhere, hanging on in sunshine and in rain. Cars are so commonly flagged down by people who need a ride that one gets into the habit of picking up people wherever one is going, because one is privileged enough to have transportation. There were times, though, when I wished to be alone, to travel at my speed and to stop wherever I wanted.

There were times, too, when I got very sick of the smell of *doma*, the betel nut which so many people chew in Bhutan. It has a particular smell, which makes me feel sick, especially when I am getting a cold. Then I looked the other way when I passed someone walking and drove as if no one was there. Most of the time people understood this remoteness, but people from the forest, people from isolated farms and poor people had a hard time with this indifference to their needs. If the weather was wet and cold, how could a driver not pick up needy people? As a result, driving in an empty can was a privilege I indulged in only when my own needs were pressing.

ROSA MACROPHYLLA Lindley

5 cm

Dochu La, Bhutan
June 30, 1990.

🌿 *Rosa macrophylla* Lindley
🌿 *Rosa brunonii* Lindley

5 cm

ROSA BRUNONII Lindley

AkHelhim
July 1, 1990
Hungso, Bhutan.

One time, when I really wanted to be alone, I went painting by Yosepang on the road between Simtokha and Dochu *La*. The weather was sunny and warm—it was nearly the end of June—and the large pink rose (*Rosa macrophylla*) growing wild up there was finished lower down. I knew it would not be flowering much longer. There was little time to waste if I wanted to capture its character and beauty on paper.

So, I drove up to Yosepang and up to Hungtso, where the rough road takes off to the Changaphug valley and where the toll station is located. But the rose was not to be seen anywhere. So I drove slowly down again towards Simtokha and saw one bush on the other side of a creek. I stopped the car and was in the process of locking it up when an old man came up to me, hat in hand, and asked, "Thimphu?" He spoke so softly I almost did not hear him.

"No," I said, smiling, and walked down the slope to the creek and across to the other side. He looked questioningly at me as I left but said nothing more. He just stood as if he was testing what would happen next.

I got to the rose, cut off a branch and sat down to draw and paint. Unbeknownst to me, the man had followed silently. Now he stood there, right in front of where I sat. He didn't say a word, and then he sat down beside me, cross-legged. The drawing took about an hour. When I finished he took the sheet from me and held up the twig and said, "Hmmmm." He sighed, exhaled, and without another sound passed both back to me, sat down again with his legs crossed, closed his eyes and entered a state of meditation; he seemed to have left me.

At the very moment I finished painting and stopped to view what had been done, he came back to the present moment. He opened his eyes and looked at me with such peace in his eyes that it made me feel warm inside.

Again he took the painting and the twig and again he looked at them for some time, glancing from one to the other and back again. Then a grin spread over his old and wrinkled face as he nodded, saying something in Dzongkha which I could not understand. We got up and he followed me to the car and again said softly, "Thimphu?" This time I nodded and motioned to him to get in on the passenger side, marvelling at his persistence and feeling a kind of reverence for a man who could show so much patience. Nearly two hours had lapsed and he had found time to seek inner peace and to share this with me. What a gift for such a short ride.

We did not speak for the entire ride back to Thimphu, but when we got to Shop 7 on the main street, he motioned to me to stop by touching my arm gently. And here we parted company. He placed the palms of his hands together and raised them to touch his nose, nearly, and then he smiled that same peaceful smile he had shared with me up the hill. He bowed his head at the same time and said, "*Kadinche*," which means "thank you." Then he turned his back to me and disappeared in the busy crowd of the main street.

Mabberley says that there are a hundred north-temperate rose species in the world, and that people have hybridized many eastern and western species, creating many hybrids with diploidy—doubling of chromosome numbers—and even triploid hybrids, with three times the standard number of seven chromosomes.

Whatever humans try to increase nature's beauty, nothing can compare to the wild rose with its simple corolla of five petals. More petals does not mean more beauty, for the wild rose is often so shy and unassuming that no tampering could improve its charm.

Another wild rose which grows in the Hungtso area is *Rosa brunonii*. It has white petals and is not very showy. It is more common than *R. macrophylla*. The hips, or berries, of this rose can be eaten. They, like others, contain vitamin C in their fleshy pulp. They make good jams, but the seeds are embedded in a hairy packing that can cause bad itches if you happen to get some down your back or into your clothes. ✳

Living in the moment

When you are poor, as the Bhutanese are poor in that they own few things, you live closer, somehow, to the intuitive level of being. You are more in tune with your surroundings; you are more flexible and more able and free to change and to adapt to new possibilities and opportunities as they arise. And so among the Bhutanese the genius of the moment has full play.

It had been raining heavily during the first monsoon rains in May 1989, and the creeks were overflowing. Old culverts were unable to carry the extra water quickly enough, and roads would wash out unless road crews got there first. In some places, the water flowed onto the roadbed and stood in wide pools.

One culvert on the road at Taba between Thimphu and Dechhenchholing was unable to take the heavy flow of water because the old stone culvert was partly clogged with sand, rocks and plastic debris. Water flowed over the roadbed nearly every time it rained heavily.

One day a red car approached the puddle from Dechhenchholing. It came to an abrupt halt in the middle of the water and both doors flew open. A barefoot woman and man got out, rags in hand. For a few hectic minutes these two people washed and wiped their car, making it look sparkling clean. Then they got into the car again and drove off. There is not really much traffic between the capital and the old palace where the third king used to live, except for military transports, some taxi jeeps and the occasional bus. Was the couple planning to return to this puddle to wash their car again in the future? I kept watching whenever I could, but I never saw them. ✳

And so among the Bhutanese the genius of the moment has full play.

A pokeweed

Rumex nepalensis belongs to the buckwheat family and is therefore relatively closely related to the buckwheat *Fagopyrum*, which is grown as a crop in Bhutan. The roots of pokeweed are used medicinally according to Polunin and Stainton (1984), though they do not state its specific curative power. It is a common plant in ruderal, or disturbed, areas in the Thimphu valley, just as many members of the same genus are in Canada. This genus has about 200 temperate species worldwide. Some are very useful plants.

Aside from being persistent weeds, the leaves of some species can be used in salads. Others have roots from which tannin can be extracted, and others still produce juices that can be used to remove rust stains from linen cloth. Others yet can be used for their yellow dyes. Generally, they grow in acid soils. Pokeweed is persistent where it grows because its seeds can lie dormant for nearly ninety years and still germinate (Mabberley, 1987). ✳

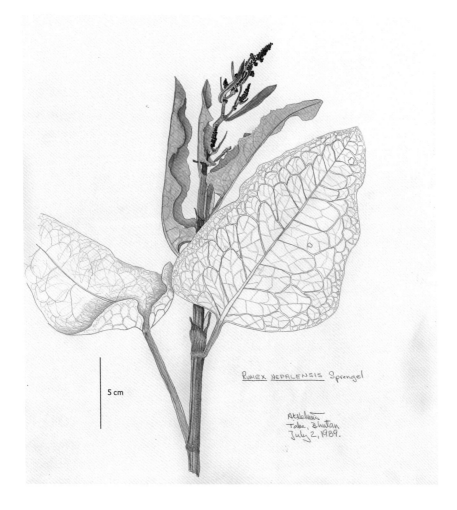

5 cm

RUMEX NEPALENSIS Sprengel

Atchelum
Toba, Bhutan
July 2, 1989.

An auspicious time

July falls in the middle of the rainy monsoon season. It can rain then solidly for days in the Thimphu valley, but the mornings are often sunny and warm, albeit humid and steamy in the rising sun.

This day, July 7, was the last day set aside for climbing up to the Phajoding *gompa*, to draw and paint. A *gompa* is a solitary temple building. I had promised the *drungtso* at the Traditional Medicine Hospital that I would paint four plants for him that were especially important medicinally. One was *Euphorbia griffithii* because at higher altitudes its roots are rich in white sap which is used as medicine. Another was *Aconitum ferox*, which is poisonous to cattle and humans. These roots are dried and powdered and given in small dosages to patients with stomach problems. The third plant I painted that day was *Rhododendron andropogon*, because its leaves are mixed with juniper to make incense for Buddhist ceremonies. I cannot remember the fourth species I painted, but while I was at Phajoding I picked this *Pedicularis* (*P. megalantha*). I painted it only after I had carried it down in the dusk of that day to Taba, where I had electric light. The genus *Pedicularis*, commonly known as "lousewort," was thought in the past to give sheep lice. The roots of the species of this genus apparently contain alkaloids, and cattle avoid them when grazing. Many members of the genus are at least partly parasitic on other plants.

July 7 was a Sunday, and it was the only day that I could spare for such a venture. The chief compounder of medicines at the hospital had to come along to find and identity the four medicinal plants. He worked six days a week in the hospital, and this was his only free day. A translator had to come along to make everything possible. All four plants grew at or above 3,600 m in altitude, over 1,200 m above Thimphu. Normally the climb takes over two hours, if you do not stop along the way to rest too often. We used only two hours that day, and the two Bhutanese men did not even seem out of breath by the time we reached the *gompa*. I, however, could only pant and shiver with cold, for I was soaking wet with sweat and the morning wind was pushing the cold fog around slowly.

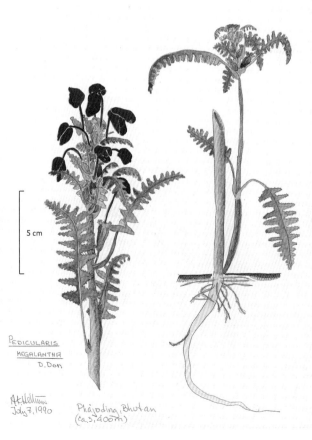

5 cm

PEDICULARIS
MEGALANTHA
D. Don

At Helliun
July 7, 1990

Phajoding, Bhutan
(ca. 3,400 m)

🌾 *Pedicularis megalantha* D. Don

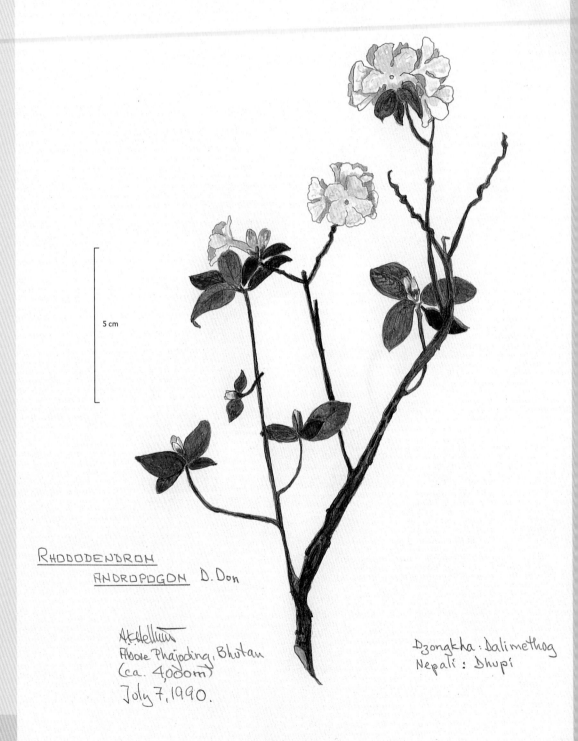

5 cm

RHODODENDRON
ANDROPOGON D. Don

A.K. Hellum
Above Phajoding, Bhutan
(ca. 4,000m)
July 7, 1990.

Dzongkha: Dalimethog
Nepali: Dhupi

We were driven up a rough bush road above Mutigthang, a high subdivision of Thimphu, to the trailhead. We started our climb from there. There was no one else around at five in the morning in the drizzling rain, as the first hints of daylight seeped into the sodden grey of night. There were no birds singing. The trees were dark silhouettes, the brush was dripping wet, the soil slick with surface runoff, the clouds weaving in and out among the trees like gauze drapery. It was ghostly and very quiet, so still I could hear my own breath, sharp and rasping in my throat. How would I keep up with these two young men striding ahead so easily?

"Tired?"

"No, just unable to speak."

For two hours we climbed steadily, stopping only here and there to discuss this plant and that. How inadequate Latin was then for remembering plants or describing them, how infinitely rich the Dzongkha words were, each name meaning something that helped someone to remember what they had seen. We climbed through blue pine forests into spruce and fir, and from spruce and fir into juniper scrub, rhododendrons and *Piptanthus*. Finally we came into lush alpine and subalpine meadows, just below the *gompa*, ripe with flowers and bees humming in their search for pollen and nectar. All the while the rain fell and hissed as it hit the grass. I was already drenched, but with sweat. I was comforted by the telling nod of the first monk we met. He glanced at his watch, nodded approvingly at our early arrival and smiled a warm welcome as we came into the courtyard of the *gompa*. Now my job was just starting.

At first, it didn't seem as if there was a dry place any place to sit. How to paint with water-colours in the rain and mist? I had to find shelter somewhere, but houses in Bhutan often have no glass in their windows and they are not heated. The fog and the humid air penetrated every nook and cranny, absolutely everywhere. Bodies scurried here and there in the soupy fog, and even the barking of the yapping dogs was muted by the gloominess of this day. It seemed a place of spirits and magic all around us. Which century was I in? The grey stone and mud buildings were timeless and the red-robed monks and attendants would be there next century as they had been for countless ones before. This place of whispers and shadows was for matters of the spirit. A fine place to be, despite the cold and wet.

"Sit here?" the translator suggested pointing up the stairs to the stoop before the entrance to the temple. A roof kept most of the rain off the stoop except when breezes wafted in. The moisture settled on my face like a salve, and my paper, even thick bristol board, became limp and soft. My pencil made grooves in the paper no matter how lightly I tried to draw.

Within minutes of when I sat down to draw the *Euphorbia*, the cold so penetrated every bone and muscle in my body I could not draw a steady line. Feeling left my right arm. It became numb. The climb was simply too rigorous for concentration and drawing, and my sweat chilled me to the point of my teeth chattering. Two young monks noticed this and scurried inside to fetch two huge red woollen blankets from their bedrolls. They draped them over my shoulders with great care not to disturb my concentration. Soon only my head poked through and my hand with the pencil. The bristol board lay on my crossed legs, on top of the red blanket folded about me so carefully. What joy to know that strangers really cared that much for me and what I was about.

At one point a monk came to hold the plant for me, and later another monk came, hunkered down beside me and for the longest time sat as if he wanted to probe my concentration and my mind. His mind was questioning mine: "What is your journey?" is what I kept hearing. But even though I tried to reach him with my mind he was mute and still. Then, as silently as he had come, he left.

The two Bhutanese men returned, dripping wet and flushed with exertion, with the other three species of medicinal plants. They had climbed up to 4,000 m to find them. They were hungry and ate their food while talking in whispers beside me. They disrobed to wring out their woolen *ghos*, and they dumped water out of their runners, but they were not cold. The Bhutanese are remarkably resistant to cold and seem to walk with more spring in their step the higher they climb, quite in contrast to Westerners.

But enough is enough: after waiting patiently for three hours while I drew and painted feverishly to finish all illustrations, they suggested we go down again to Thimphu. After all, it would be dark again in a couple of hours. But we had to wait until my last painting was dry enough not to smear before we could go down. That took nearly an hour and even then I worried about damage. It took us less time to descend than to climb up and the descent was made more joyful by the company of two girls and a man who had come up the day before to stay at the *gompa* and fetch holy water from a nearby spring.

When the doctor at the Traditional Medicine Hospital realized that the illustrations had been made on the stoop of the *gompa* he said, "Very auspicious," meaning the place had been right for giving these four illustrations special power and meaning. ✳

A composite plant at Taba

Members of the Ligularia genus (Ligularia fischeri) resemble those of the *Senecio* of the same composite family. This is a tall, stately plant that inhabited wet soils in Taba, where I lived.

    I painted this plant towards the end of July in 1989. It was growing in a thicket of many water-loving plants. Its bracts are sometimes as long as the petals of the individual flowers contained in each inflorescence, or group of individual flowers. There were two kinds of flowers in this inflorescence: ray florets and disc florets. The five petals of the marginal ray florets are fused into a strap-like yellow petal. The leaves are toothed but not dissected, and their stems clasp the flowering stalk. They are nearly round in shape with a long petiole. ✳

55

This is a tall, stately plant that inhabited wet soils in Taba, where I lived.

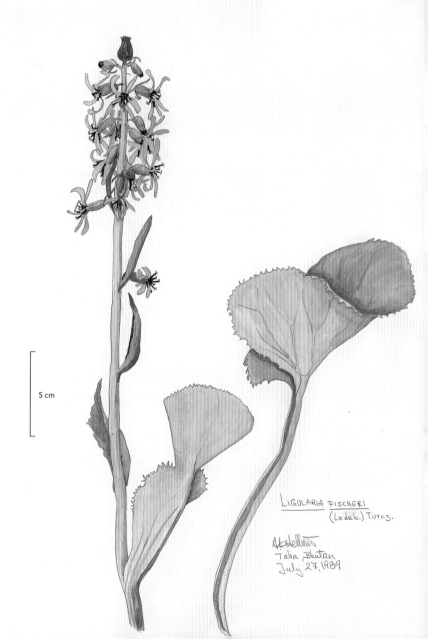

5 cm

LIGULARIA FISCHERI
(Ledeb.) Turcz.

Taba Bhutan
July 27, 1989

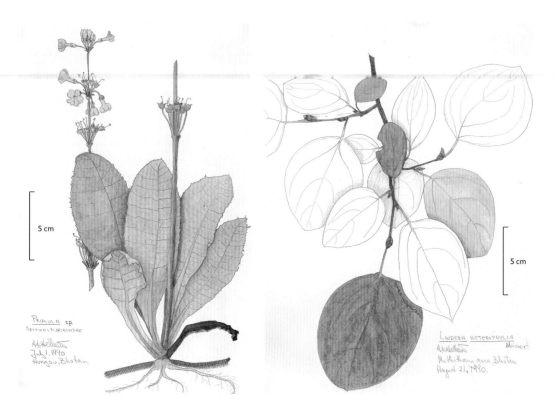

PRIMULA SP.
SECTION : FLORIBUNDAE

July 1, 1990
Hungsu, Bhutan

LINDERA HETEROPHYLLA
Meisner

Motithang area Bhutan
August 21, 1990.

56

A primula at Hungtso

This primula belongs to the section of the genus called *Floribundae*, or "abundant
flowers," because it has several whorls of flowers on the same flowering stalk. This species might
be *Primula floribunda* Wallich, but I could not tell for certain because my plant identification keys
were inadequate. Most primulas do not have more than one whorl. There are 400 north-
temperate species in the world and forty-three species are identified in Polunin and Stainton's
book (1984), which covers only some of the species found in Nepal. They state that this genus
has its greatest concentration of species in the Himalayas. I can believe that, for the flowers grew
everywhere in northwestern Bhutan.

Most primulas flower during the spring, summer and fall, but two species flowered year-round
in the Thimphu valley, even during snows and when nights were freezing cold.

Lindera heterophylla is a valuable plant. It belongs to the laurel family. There are some eighty
species in this genus in the world, mostly tropical and temperate. The leaves of this genus have
been used to make tea, the wood is aromatic, and the flowers have been used as an allspice substitute (Mabberley, 1987). The bark has been used to reduce fever. This species is common in the
Thimphu valley. ❁

❧ *Primula* sp. L   ❧ *Lindera heterophylla* Meisn.
❧ *Lilium* sp. L

5 cm

10 cm

LILIUM

A.K.Helliwu
August 31, 1990
Top of Changaphug valley, Bhutan
ca. 3,800 m.

Lily and rhubarb up Changaphug valley

In spring, summer and early fall in Bhutan, it is impossible for a painter to keep up with the abundance of flowering plants. Many flower and set seed before it is possible to catch them on paper. This was the case for this lily. It was flowering in mid-August when I had been up the Changaphug valley, but by the end of the month it had finished, and its seeds were maturing. There are about 100 species of this genus in north-temperate climates. This one had large, white flowers.

There is one lily in Bhutan said to have medicinal uses, but I do not know if this is the right species.

The roots of *Rheum acuminatum* are used medicinally, according to Polunin and Stainton. It grows at altitudes from 3,600 to 4,500 m in Nepal; I found it growing at about 4,000 m in the Changaphug valley, above timber-line. It too had flowered before the end of August, so I could only draw the dried-out plant. It too, like the *Rumex* species discussed earlier, belongs to the buckwheat family. ❋

58

RHEUM ACUMINATUM
Hook. f. & Thoms. ex Hook.
At top of Changaphug
Valley, Bhutan

August 31, 1990.

5 cm

Many flower
and set seed before
it is possible to
catch them on paper.
This was the case
for this lily.

❧ *Rheum acuminatum* Hook. f. & Thomas. ex Hook.

Fall

The nights were clear, cool and crisp,
and the days were sunny and warm,
and sometimes windy.

5 cm

ACONITUM FEROX Seringe

September 30, 1990.
Dochu La, Bhutan

Fall

FALL HAS ALWAYS BEEN A SEASON MIXED with sadness and joy for me, sadness for the passing of summer, and maybe also for the coming of winter cold, and joy for the wonderful clarity of fall days when it feels as if I should hold my breath lest I scare the warmth away. In fall in Bhutan, I would have started to wind down the sometimes busy schedule of summer, except for the pressure to paint yet more flowers before night frosts did them in. The fall of 1989 in northwest Bhutan was much like fall in Alberta, Canada. The nights were clear, cool and crisp, and the days were sunny and warm, and sometimes windy.

September is a month for celebration in Thimphu. This is when the Thimphu *chechu* is held, a magnificent celebration of history, glory, colour and community. Hundreds of people come from the hillsides and distant communities, carrying their food with them, to see the ceremonies. My son Timothy had just come to visit me when the *chechu* took place. He had just left Ryerson Polytechnic in Toronto, Canada, where he was studying photography, and he brought hundreds of rolls of film with him. I think he shot most of them during the three days of the *chechu*. *National Geographic* had sent a photographer to the same *chechu* and Timothy watched him, absorbing ideas like a blotter. The weather was bright; light, puffy clouds drifted above in a blue, blue sky and the colours of the clothes worn then were intoxicating for a person with a camera. People dressed up in their finery for the occasion.

Aconitum ferox Wall. ex Seringe

Everyone came to the courtyard of the Tashichhodzong, the seat of government in Bhutan, to watch the traditional dances and the jokers who went about with masks. Children's laughter could be heard almost continually, bursting forth now and then into loud cheers. All the dances were performed by men, and their garb was exotic, colourful and elegant. They danced barefoot, their eyes peering out through the mouths of the wooden masks they wore as they moved in large circles around in the cobbled courtyard.

I have never seen a more enthralled audience anywhere. Some people would sit with their food in their hands, ready to eat, watching the dancers, and they would forget to eat. This was real stuff for the imagination, battles fought and won, spirits chased away, demons exorcised, shouts of triumph mingled with laughter and encouragement from the actors—shields, swords, drums, masks, confrontations and imagined battles, all the stuff of legend and pride in nation. I thought these events were similar to storytelling in Norway or Iceland a millennium ago: oral tradition at its very best. It felt as if the heroes and demons were among us, challenging us, threatening us, and the heroes finally saving us from terrible fates. I felt elevated and happy to be alive.

When the *chechu* was over, people drifted away to their daily tasks. I put away the *gho* I had bought for the *chechu*. Somehow we had to come down to earth again. It was time for more sober thoughts. With fall came colder—sometimes freezing—nights, and bright, sunny days with crisp air and temperatures above +20°C at midday. With fall I had to scramble to stock up on oak wood for the colder months ahead. If I wasn't quick, it would all be sold. I had to find someone to transport, split and stack it, if it was to dry before it could be burned. It was cut green.

This was the time when I travelled into the Dochu *La* and Chele *La* to draw and paint. The highest mountains already had dustings of snow by October, and the rice harvesting kept people very busy lower down. Fall in Bhutan was a time for gathering and storing foods and fuel for the winter, just as in any other temperate climate. I could feel an urgency about living that was infectious, even though instead of fruits or vegetables to harvest I had plants to paint before they withered on the stalk. From the second-storey window of my apartment, I could see red chilis and meat strips drying on rooftops everywhere. The weekly Thimphu market had wonderful and strange vegetables for us to buy, and chanterelle mushrooms for sale at very low prices. We ate to our hearts' delight.

I drove to Chele *La* to paint gentians. They flower by day and wither by night in October, when temperatures swing from -15°C at night to above +20°C at midday. Some flowers lasted only a day; other species revived in the daytime after seeming to freeze at night, and some closed their flower heads as nighttime approached and then opened them again after sunrise the following day. I wanted to experience all this activity, for I had been told that the change from day to night, from sundown to sunrise, from rain to sunshine was remarkable, and I was not disappointed. All of a sudden there were flowers that I had never seen before, poking only their heads out of the ground, and then they were gone by the next sunrise.

Gentianella pedunculata (D. Don) Harry Smith, above; *Gentiana* sp. L, below

GENTIANELLA
PEDUNCULATA
(D. Don) Harry Smith

5 cm

A.K. Mellin
October 22, 1989
Chele La, Bhutan
above 4,000 m.

$* K_{(5)} [C_{(5)} A_{(5)}] G_{(\underline{2})}$ capsule

Calyx
tubular

GENTIANA sp.

A.K. Mellin
October 22, 1989
Chele La, Bhutan
above 4,000 m.

These plants are very poisonous, and at the same time they are very important medicinally to the Bhutanese.

My problem was that the water froze in my paints, and my hands got so cold I could not draw a straight line until things thawed out after sunrise. I couldn't paint after sundown, because temperatures dropped almost instantly below freezing.

I painted monkshood, *Aconitum ferox*, which derives its name from the shape of its hooded flowers. These plants are very poisonous, and at the same time they are very important medicinally to the Bhutanese. The roots, when ground up, help ease stomach ailments, if taken in appropriately small doses.

Sometimes, when I would come upon whole fields of this monkshood in bloom, I would sit down and watch it while the winds rippled across the heads of the plants, making them sway on their thin stalks. Like waves of the ocean, I thought. Bhutan has its oceans: oceans of flowers.

I went from flower to flower and from place to place painting as if I were possessed. It was an overwhelming job. I could only sample from the abundance. The question was which plants to capture in my paints, and which to leave behind. One of the flowering shrubs I could not resist was *Indigofera*. Plants from this genus are still used in India and on Sumatra for dye-making, but indigo has elsewhere lost out to synthetic dyes. I do not know of its use in Bhutan for similar purposes. I could not identify this particular plant—one example of many I encountered on my wanderings—to species for lack of a complete flora.

The alpine meadows looked absolutely magnificent in fall, and I worked frantically, catching primulas, asters, edelweisses, gentianellas and ephedras with their bright red fruits. I would go to bed at night dreaming of plants I had not been able to draw for lack of enough daylight and energy. I felt like a child at Christmas with a tree full of candy and gingerbread cookies all to myself, but with only one evening to eat everything.

At sunset, the mountain passes and meadows really fill with magic as insects buzz about and winds play hide-and-seek. Then the Chele *La* was so clear and still that I could see far into Sikkim to the west, valley beyond valley, and when the air can be so still that a lit match burns still and straight.

One morning in October 1989, the sun rose and coloured the snows of the peak of Jumolhary pink. Frozen dew on everything twinkled in the new light. At such times I felt so cold I would shake, and not even dry wood would burn for me. Within minutes of awakening, I just wanted to sit down to soak up the warmth and promise in the air. That is when I wrote the following lines, when the day was so young and so fresh and the day's work seemed so grey and uninteresting.

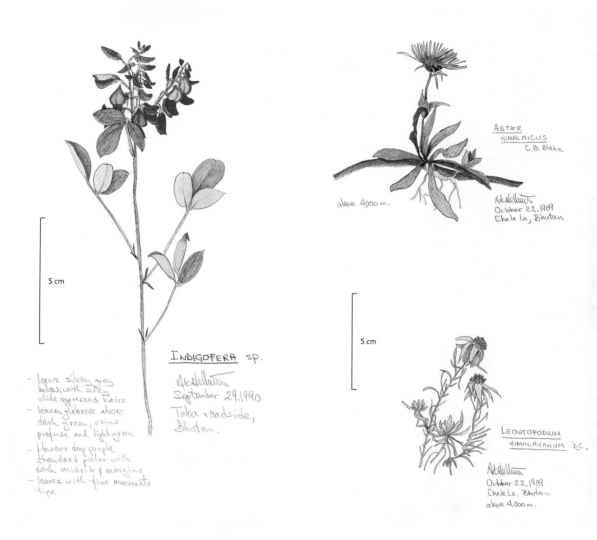

ASTER
HIMALAICUS
C.B. Blake

above 4000 m.

Ackellums
October 22, 1989
Chele La, Bhutan

5 cm

INDIGOFERA SP.

Ackellums
September 29,1990
Tsloa roadside,
Bhutan.

- leaves silvery grey
below, with silky
white appressed hairs
- leaves glabrous above
dark green, veins
profuse and light green
- flowers deep purple
standard paler with
dark midrib & margins
- leaves with fine mucronate
tips.

5 cm

LEONTOPODIUM
HIMALAYANUM DC.

Ackellums
October 22, 1989
Chele La, Bhutan
above 4,000 m.

Come take your chair to the morning sun.
Come feel how it can warm you.
The day is long 'fore the work is done.
Come sit now I implore you.

As I sat in the grass at sunrise in Chele *La* a small aster started to open its petals, as if an eye was looking up at me. I took out my pad and my paints and started to put this smile to paper. ❋

❧ *Indigofera* sp. L

❧ *Aster himalaicus* C.B. Blake, above; and *Leontopodium himalayanum* DC., below

5 cm

ORYZA sp.

St Helens
October 25, 1989
Namseling, Bhutan

The last harvest

After the rice harvest comes winter.

One late December day in 1988, two friends and I walked up to the Phajoding *gompa* above Thimphu. We spent the night there so we could walk higher the next day. As we stumbled out of our sleeping bags to greet the first rays of sun, I could look way down over the Thimphu valley and see the smoke rising from the many fires where women were preparing for the day. The smoke hovered around the valley bottom as long as the sun was only shining above the valley floor. But when it reached the houses, and warmed them, the smoke started to rise up the slopes. Convectional flow, I thought. By the time we had eaten breakfast and donned our packs, the smoke was covering the landscape in a haze. Home-grown pollution, I thought, not smog from the lowlands as I had thought before.

Two days later, when we again descended to the Phajoding *gompa* after our hike above 4,000 m, the cold air from higher up was sliding down the valley sides and clarity was returning to the higher places. Again convectional flow, I thought. Then I thought that this cycle probably repeated itself every day of the year. To catch sight of these mountain peaks from valley bottom I had to get up very early, before the sun started to warm my world, and before home fires were again lit in preparation for the coming day.

In October, as the last rice *(Oryza)* is harvested, this convectional cycle was repeating itself day after day. We found later, in the Changaphug valley, that the only wind movement in that valley in the fall of 1989 was convectional, only up and down the slope. I knew this because virtually no tree seed fell in the clear-cut strips made up and down the slope here. It all fell within the intervening forests.

The rice at Namseling, a short distance south from Thimphu, seemed to ripen last of all in the Thimphu valley where the Wang *Chu* flows. The village crews had already harvested the rice at Namseling when I got there, but a few stalks remained, escapees from the sickle. The crews move from paddy field to paddy field helping each other until the job is done.

In the Thimphu valley people grow both white and pinkish red rice. The red rice tasted more glutinous than the white rice. These varieties are specially adapted to this temperate climate and high altitude, growing at about 1,000 m higher in altitude than regular rice from the lowlands. The fields look different:

The white rice plants look golden at maturity and at harvest time, while the red rice looks browner from a distance.

Oryza sp. L.

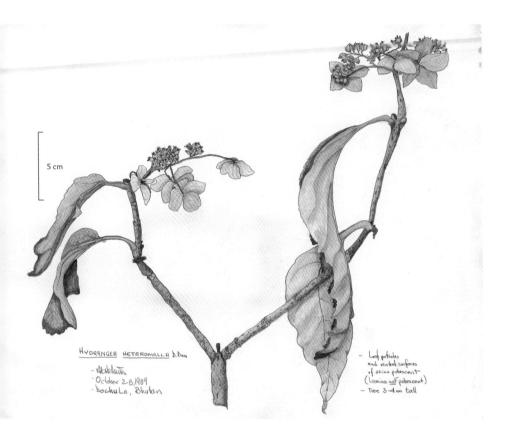

5 cm

HYDRANGEA HETEROMALLA D.Don

- Watercolour
- October 2-8, 1989
- Dochu La, Bhutan

- Leaf petioles
  and ventral surfaces
  of veins pubescent
  (Lamina not pubescent)
- Tree 3-4 m tall

The last flowers of fall

Edelweiss, edelweiss, show me your bloom, show me your bloom in the morning's sun, show me your velvet-like flowers.

So, it isn't only the Swiss and the Italians and the Austrians who have these strange flowers, I thought when I found this edelweiss in the Chele *La*. They grow in profusion in the Himalayas. That was a revelation. Since seeing them for the first time, I have learned that several species grow in the Himalayas and seven grow in the Andean mountains of South America (Mabberley, 1987). The genus is cosmopolitan—what a strange, disjunct distribution.

In the Dochu *La*, at about 3,000 m, there is another late bloomer that I wanted to capture on paper. It is the tree form of hydrangea, the plant that we know in Canada as a bush with white, pink or pale blue "flowers," depending on the acidity of the soil underfoot. But the peak flowering time had passed, and the flowers had turned brown after frost.

This hydrangea, painted in late October, can grow over 10 m tall and it has a stem diameter of about 15 cm at altitudes over 2,800 m. I found it in spruce and hemlock forests in the Dochu *La*. The brown petal-like parts are not in fact petals or sepals but bracts. They are pink and white when the plant is in full bloom.

🌿 *Hydrangea heteromalla* D. Don
🌿 *Sambucus adnata* Wallich ex DC.

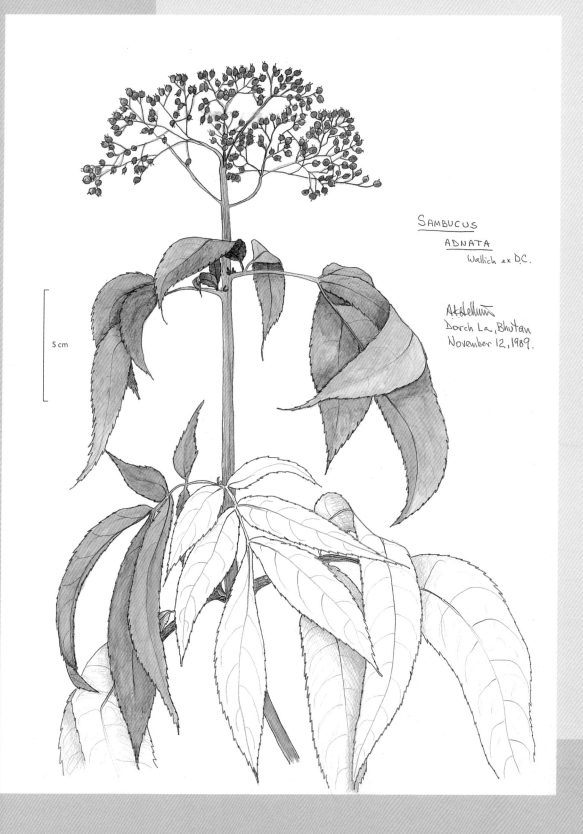

SAMBUCUS

ADNATA

Wallich ex D.C.

Asteltium

Dorch La, Bhutan

November 12, 1989.

5 cm

I also painted the elderberry, called *Sambucus adnata*. I wanted to show it to friends to ask them if they collected the berries off this species for making jellies, jams, wines or other alcoholic drinks. But no one used it. This plant grew in the Dochu *La*. Some species in other parts of the world yield a blue dye from crushed berries.

Fall is a lingering time for me; I love the warm days that can stretch like fingers of a hand into winter. Brief moments of warmth emerge and disappear like smoke until the cold penetrates everywhere and people start to dream of visits to warmer places.

The periods between darkness and light, between cold and warm, between night and day, those are pure poetry for me. When frost is melting and dripping to the ground like rain from trees and rooftops and flowers, when herders goad their cattle to the forests and meadows in their bare feet, when their calls sound like singing in the crispness of the air, and when the smoke has started to stir from the valley floor, that is a wonderful time for me. Then there is no place like this far-off valley in far-off Bhutan.

The minutiae of all living things were demanding centre stage once more for me, and I wanted to soak up the stillness and the awakening beauty around me. This was the time when people would light smudge fires in altar places all around where I lived, with cypress and cedar, juniper and rhododendron. I was told that the smoke fed the hungry and invisible spirits who live on scents. When I heard the faint tinkle of bells in these early hours, it was as if I had come to a feast where the tables were laid and the trumpets sounded in welcome. I felt a part of this thanksgiving. Polish the rice before eating. Polish the spirit before growing too old to pray. Be kind to your fellow humans, for their *samsara*, their destiny, may be harder than yours. Be compassionate. That is what these mornings taught me. ❁

It was not really possible to sit still for long inside houses without getting close to a stove, or bukhari, to thaw out...

Winter

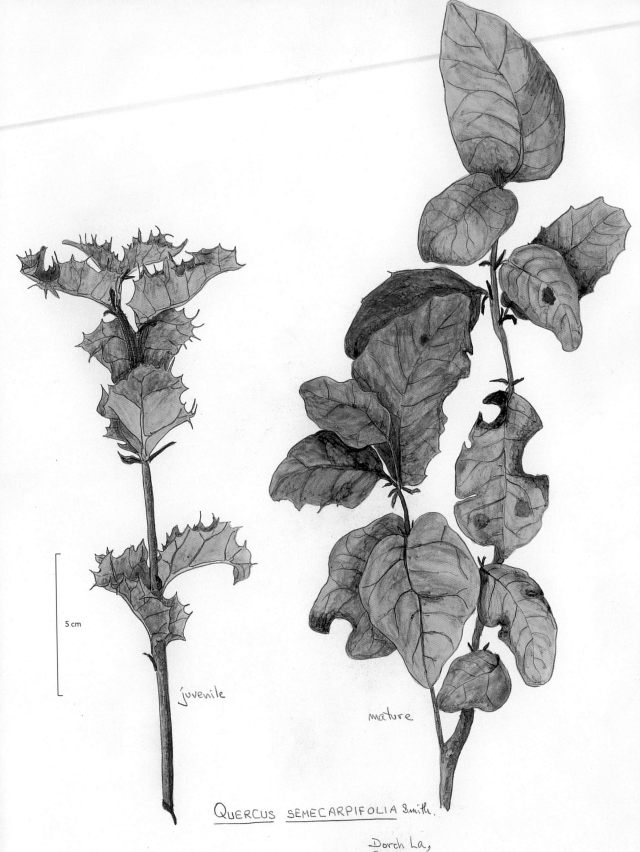

5 cm

juvenile

mature

QUERCUS SEMECARPIFOLIA Smith.

Dorch La,
Bhutan

AKHollum
3/12/88

I HAVE NEVER BEEN SO COLD IN WINTER AS IN BHUTAN. It was not really possible to sit still for long inside houses without getting close to a stove, or *bukhari*, to thaw out, or without going outside during the sunny part of the day. Some people even took their desks outside to work in the sunshine, or they took their work out on the grass and sat cross-legged. Once I saw a cow come sauntering by a man sitting on the grass working, and as it passed it took a sheet of paper from his pile, chewed it, and swallowed it. From that day on I kept thinking that data served multiple purposes in Bhutan.

It was during winter that the water-line to my rented house froze. I could never be sure that I would wake up having running water unless I let the water run all night. Once winter came, it became necessary to let the tap drip even if the air was warm when I went to bed. The dripping faucet sometimes kept me awake all night wondering if it had stopped, if it was frozen again. To be without water is something even the Bhutanese see as a problem. That was in a sense a comfort, but it was always up to me to thaw things out. I never called a plumber for that, especially after my experiences in the Thimphu hotel.

Winter really came in December, not just because the nights were cold but because the days were noticeably shorter even though Bhutan lies only a few degrees north of the tropics. It was a time for painting conifers rather than deciduous plants, and for concentrating on the intricacies of cones, seeds and fruits.

Quercus semecarpifolia Smith

The oak (*Quercus semecarpifolia*) is the prized fuel wood of central Bhutan, and especially of the Thimphu valley. The Bhutanese prefer it to the blue pine, with its resins and tar, but it is not always available from the yard of the Department of Forestry even for those who can afford to buy it rather than collecting it from the hills themselves. Only the wealthier city folks can afford to pay for wood. Most wood is gathered by local people who ascend the hills before dawn, climbing hundreds of meters to find suitable wood. Then, as daylight comes, the men and young boys come back home with huge bundles on their backs, tied with rope to their shoulders. They carry small pieces of wood and branches, mostly. They leave the beautiful, straight, tall trees alone because they are too heavy and difficult to carry and they take too much energy to fell in the first place.

The yaks and cattle also use this oak for food. The yaks come down from their pastures in winter and the cattle come up into the higher country in summer to where the oak grows. The oak, which is evergreen, grows at altitudes between 2,200 and 3,500 m. Often the same area gets grazed all year in this way.

How does the tree survive this pressure? One way is that it produces spiny leaves. Young leaves are always hairy beneath and very prickly to the touch, but not enough so to be left alone by the animals. Another way is that this oak produces an abundance of shoots from old stumps or from the bases of older trees. In fact, without some pruning, these sprouts will not grow to produce good wood for fuel or lumber, but in general the grazing is detrimental to the growth of new shoots. The abundance of young, spiny leaves on most oaks of this species in the whole Thimphu area embodies the tree's struggle against the heavy grazing and cutting going on.

The winding road going east from Simtokha to Hungtso passes through dense patches of oak where grazing animals roam. In these thickets, I could sit and observe the traffic or paint without being seen. On one sunny morning in December 1988 I drove up there, parked the car off the road on a small spur and settled in to paint. Tibetans came by with their cattle and with horses loaded with sacks of goods. (A large settlement of Tibetan refugees had come to live by Hungtso after China invaded Tibet in 1952.) The Tibetan women wear their hair in long braids wound around on the tops of their heads.

And the road workers came by, mostly Nepalese and Indians, in family groups with their food containers, black umbrellas and brightly coloured clothes and baskets. When the sun was hot, they put the umbrellas over the baskets to protect the babies, and when it was rainy, women and children clustered under these same shelters, talking away. Because this was a sunny winter's day, the umbrellas were folded away and the young children were running about, playing on the road, while the men chatted and shovelled soil and the women carried the soil on gunnysacks to the roadside to be dumped. These crews travel continually, cleaning up small landslips or large landslides, fallen rock, fallen trees and even snow in winter. They also paint the rocks white along the outer edges of the road, and rebuild

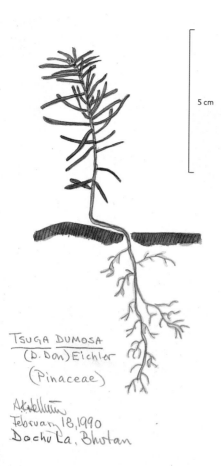

TSUGA DUMOSA
(D. Don) Eichler
(Pinaceae)

A.Kalehiin
February 18, 1990
Dochu La, Bhutan

TSUGA DUMOSA
(D. Don) Eichler

A.Kalehiin
4/12/88
Dochu La
Bhutan

concrete monuments along the roads where landslips had taken them away. Sometimes they also rebuild whole sections of road, when the roadbeds give way and disappear in the monsoon season.

The odd bus would pass by, and the odd truck loaded with goods and people would belch its way up or down the road going somewhere, painfully and laboriously. Sometimes a private car came by, and sometimes a scooter or small motorcycle would sputter past. But most of the traffic was Bhutanese walking with fuelwood bundles on their backs, men all bent over by weight, and cattle herders with their meandering flocks of cows. Even so, the road was mostly empty, and I could almost forget that this was the main link between west and east. What a peaceful place this Bhutan, how strangely alone one could feel in the middle of this stream of humanity.

Hemlock (*Tsuga dumosa*) grows in Bhutan at altitudes between 2,400 and 3,300 m. It is found mostly on east- and north-facing slopes at lower altitudes, where moisture is more plentiful than on south- and west-facing slopes. When mature, these trees develop a dome-shaped crown which can be seen for miles against the skyline or in hillside forests. Hemlock is a majestic tree.

This little drawing of a twig with cones was made up the Changaphug valley near Dochu *La*. This tree grew along the stream, spreading its long pendant branches over the gully, in the noise of the waters tumbling down. It was a gnarled tree with many cones. It had been spared the axe so far because the trunk was bent and the bark showed clear signs of spiral grain. Probably it had been growing here for over two hundred years and had seen many humans come and go.

Tsuga dumosa (D. Don) Eichler

There were the Tibetans who came to settle in the early 1950s after the Chinese invasion of their homeland. There were the monks and nuns of the Kargyudpa sect of Buddhists coming to meditate in the forest monastery high on the hill where they could devote long periods of their life to solitary meditation.

And the tree must have seen the countless woodcutters and cutters of shakes for roofs, it must have seen the cattle herders and the mendicants who roam the land in search of inner peace, and it must also have seen the mushroom gatherers and the gatherers of edible and medicinal plants over more time than you or I might care to contemplate.

Under the spread of its wide branches, little seedlings grew on a small hummock.

I painted this twig in December 1988, and the seedling in February 1990 when I came back to renew my friendship with this old tree. In between those times, the old tree had been lopped of all its branches except for a wisp at the very top. Even it had not escaped the axe. Now it stood waiting, and looking disgraced and empty of its shelter and its ability to renew itself. It was waiting now, I think, to die of starvation. Yet by being so denuded and disgraced, it might help the seedling to grow in its place.

5 cm

CUPRESSUS HIMALAICA Silba

Taba, Bhutan
December 15, 1988.

Cupressus himalaica Silba

ABIES
DENSA
Griff

AK Hellum
Taba nursery,
Bhutan
March 10, 1990.

ABIES DENSA
Griff.

AK Hellum
November 26, 1989.
Changaphug valley, Bhutan

Cupressus himalaica is the holy tree of Bhutan; the people call it *Tsenden*. It grows to 30 m in height, and the trees at Pangri Zampa, just east of Dechhenchholing, must be nearly 3 m in diameter. They are immense. Early explorers say the tree was brought to Bhutan by Tibetan monks and planted around the *gompas* there because the wood is aromatic and durable and is a favourite for building temples. If this is true, that the tree came from Tibet, then the trees at Pangri Zampa must be from Shabdrung Namgyal's time in the 1600s. Maybe they are even older. Shabdrung Namgyal came from Tibet to escape religious sect problems. He united the many small kingdoms under one rule.

Natural stands can now be found in the Po *Chu* valley and in the Pele *La* area farther east. Because it is such a valuable tree and is used so extensively for building the inner temples of the *dzongs*, the species is seriously over-exploited. There were a few experimental plantings by 1990, but no larger scale efforts were evident.

Its branches are also used in smudge fires to call upon spirits of other worlds. Altars are made from the wood, as are chests for clothes. The heartwood has a rich, reddish colour.

The native fir, *Abies densa*, grows to dimensions as large as those of hemlock and spruce: 30 m tall, with stump diameters over 60 cm. It is most commonly found along the higher forests, just below timber-line, where fogs seem to sustain the trees. When the fogs shift up or down slope, it is said that the firs die from drought. Many stands had died when I was in Bhutan. For the sake of the well-being of the country, I hope that the true cause of their death has been found by now, and that something can be done to save these majestic stands. If it has to do with climatic shifts in the lowlands, or if it has to do with climatic warming or drying, then these magnificent forests may be doomed. Their seedlings are eaten by yaks, and there are many yaks grazing just where these trees grow. These forests may need help for Mother Nature to do her job.

Abies densa Griff.

5 cm

PINUS WALLICHIANA

A.B. Jackson

December 31, 1988
Taba, Bhutan

Blue pine (*Pinus wallichiana*) is the most common tree in the Thimphu valley, as it is in most of the valleys of western Bhutan. It grows from valley floor at around 2,400 m to well over 3,000 m. In the Thimphu valley, it forms young stands spreading uphill for some distance on both sides as if some catastrophe of the past wiped it out and then allowed it to re-establish itself later. These stands are between thirty and forty years old.

Blue pine is the favourite wood for carpentry in Bhutan. Some local craftsmen swear by it, saying there is no other wood suitable for their house building—no other, that is, except for the spruce and fir they fell for shakes to cover the roofs, and the cypress used for temples.

But blue pine wood is no good as fuel. Its tars gum up chimneys, dripping black messes everywhere. Oak burns better, hotter, giving more heat, and leaves far less ash behind, too.

Last year's needles turn yellow in late autumn, just before they fall off and before cones ripen their seeds. The tree retains only one year of needles over winter. Even these turn yellowish on dry hillsides when rains are few and far between. Some winters, no rain may fall from October to April. But the foliage is normally bluish green.

5 cm

One Sunday in late December 1988, when the sun was bright and the air clear and warm, I walked high up into the hills above Thimphu and painted this pine twig and cone. Far below me lay Thimphu, surrounded by grey paddy fields in their winter rest. The land looked laced with narrow fields as if in some filigree of lead.

The sun was warm and the air balmy until about four in the afternoon. But when the sun went down behind the western hills, the water froze in my paints, and my skin got so cold it was hard to hold a brush. Red-billed *choughs* circled far above on upward currents of air, and as they flew in wide circles they drifted north, up the valley. Their cries faded into the distance. It was time to go home.

The deodar cedar (*Cedrus deodara*) is not native to Bhutan, but it is grown as an ornamental and has been planted in reforestation projects sometimes, when seeds have been available from India and Nepal. It has not grown long enough in Bhutan to reach the venerable stature reached in northern India and in Nepal, but it seems to thrive in and around Thimphu.

This branch was just disappearing down a cow's gullet when I rescued it. The branch had come from the landlord's tree, and that made me possessive. When visiting India some time later I was told that cattle do not normally eat deodar cedar seedlings, and that reforestation is possible even with lots of cattle around. But I listened only with half an ear, for by then I knew better, at least in Bhutan.

ॐ *Pinus wallichiana* A.B. Jackson

ॐ *Cedrus deodara* (Roxb. ex D. Don) G.Don.

In the relative warmth of my living room, I completed this drawing of the twig. Its whimsy and grace appealed to me just after New Year's, when I was thinking too often of spring and warmer weather.

But my concentration was interrupted by the need to thaw frozen water pipes lying on the frozen ground outside. And my legs were so cold after a while I had to move to get warm. I thought of the pipes lying there on frozen ground and in the shade of the house, and could not see how they could thaw before warmer weather came. But something had to be done and no one was going to come and do this for me. If I waited, so would the water.

Several hours later, having burned out an electric space-heater trying to thaw the pipes outside, having driven three times to Thimphu some 5 km away to buy wiring and plugs to make an extension cord, and having unwrapped the rubber inner-tube wrappings around the makeshift connections of pipe only to find trickles of water at one section after the other, I gave up and went to light the *bukhari* in the wash-house and the clay oven in the storage room of the house, to see if this would ease my predicament.

JUNIPERUS PSEUDOSABINA Fisher & Meyer

Tala, Bhutan
December 15, 1988.

🌿 *Juniperus pseudosabina* Fisher & Meyer

By early evening, I finally had running water and a house full of smoke from the old-fashioned clay oven. I felt victorious, but apprehensive about the night, when frost again would raise hell. So I kept the water running all night and for several days in a row after that too, until warmer weather came.

When all this was done there was supper to cook on the *bukhari* and dishes to wash. When darkness came and the living room was cosy and warm with an oak-wood fire, I turned on a bright light, pulled myself into a cross-legged sitting position on the couch, and concentrated once more on painting. Into the night and the stillness, and into a restful state of mind, I ventured.

When all was said and done, I felt thankful for my solitude. During such days it was hard to deal with the needs of others as well as my own, and I was glad that I had not subjected any of my family members to this problem of water in winter.

I slept well that January night in 1989, knowing that all was well with the water and therefore with my life. Problems were basic in Bhutan.

Juniperus pseudosabina is a large tree-form juniper. It can grow to about 20 m tall with a diameter of 30 cm or more at breast-height. Its seeds are slow germinators, and as a result seedlings can establish themselves at most times of the year. The tree looks very much like the western red cedar (*Thuja plicata*) that grows along the Pacific coast of North America, except for its cones, which have scales shaped like shields. It is used as a substitute for cedar where aromatic wood is desired, and it makes excellent fuel, and it is usually left undisturbed when logging for spruce and pine. It grows at altitudes between 2,800 and 3,500 m in the vicinity of Thimphu. Its foliage is used for incense in early-morning smudges to appease the spirits and gods. ❄

The bath

It is no surprise in Bhutan that people are loath to take baths. It is too cold for much of the year, and the houses are not heated. All through winter, people try to keep warm. Office hours are shortened to 9 a.m. to 4 p.m. (from 8 a.m. to 5 p.m. in summer) because when the sun goes down it is simply too difficult to sit in government offices and work at desks. It is necessary to move about to keep warm.

But when the Bhutanese decide to take baths, they use the same type of tubs they have been using for centuries. They dig a hole in the ground the size of a sit-bath down by a stream with running water, even in winter. They line this hole with heavy planks. Then they build a small fire next to the tub and heat stones until they are hot. When the stones are hot enough, they lead some water from the creek into the tub and roll in some hot stones. When the water is steaming and more than tepid, they strip and jump in.

You can find these bathtubs along many walking trails in Bhutan. You can find one along the trail to Taktsang, for example, and one along the trail from Dechhenchholing to Punakha. The Punakha trail was part of the old "highway" between the winter seat of the Buddhist religion in Bhutan and the summer seat in Thimphu. The monks walked this trail east every fall when they wanted to live in Punakha and then west again in spring when they walked back into the Thimphu valley. Most of the early visitors to Bhutan in the last two centuries travelled this trail too. It is well-worn even today, but the monks now drive from Punakha to Thimphu and back. They do not have to make the day-long walk. But local people still walk with their pack-horses, and others now live in small groups of houses along the trail. It can be a very busy thoroughfare when people come to the weekend market at Thimphu and then return home late on Sundays or early on Mondays.

On one bright spring day I awoke, got dressed, ate a hurried breakfast, packed some fruit, a bottle of drinking water and my painting materials, and headed for the Punakha trail to paint.

After about 15 minutes' walk from Dechhenchholing there is a stream crossing where a communal bathtub is dug into the side of the hill. It is just beside the trail. As I rounded a curve in the trail just before this place I heard singing—wonderful Bhutanese singing. It sounded like a young man's voice. As I got closer, I could see the steam and realized someone was having a Sunday morning bath as the sun was searching out the ground, having just sailed from behind the mountains to the east. The hoarfrost was on the ground still in shaded places. The night had been cool and the air was standing still, except for the very light stirrings of the wind up the valley and trail from lower reaches. The air was fresh and clean and filled with forest smells of pine and fir and damp soil along the stream.

When I passed the tub and the man in it, I could see only the occasional arm poking its way through the steam. The song would have enveloped him even if the steam had not. His clothes lay in a heap right by the place where I knew the tub was. A small draft of air moved the steam enough that I saw his face, his hair white with soap. He must have heard me for he stopped singing, looked intently at me, and then raised an arm and waved, palm facing me. He shouted something in Dzongkha and laughed. I raised my arm, palm towards him in embarrassed greeting. I said something in English and then hurried by. He looked after me and then returned to his bath.

When I rounded the next corner in the trail, I could hear his singing again, but it faded as I walked up the trail and away.

There is a Bhutanese custom that you talk to everyone you meet on any trail. It is common courtesy to strike up a small conversation, but not one too curious to rob the passer-by of his privacy. What better place but from a hot and comfortable bathtub early on a Sunday's morning in early spring?✳

What an ideal place to be if you really wanted to meet people.

Primula irregularis Craib

In a snowstorm

primulas of all sorts of colours, sizes and shapes abound in western Bhutan, from the nearly ever-flowering *Primula denticulata* to this one, *Primula irregularis,* found at Dochu *La* in the fir forest. There are blue-flowered species and yellow-flowered species, mauve ones and greenish ones, white ones and deep red ones. Flowers with yellow centres are most common, but some have white centres and some have multi-flowered stalks.

This plant flowered in the Dochu *La* in mid-February 1990 in the middle of a snowstorm. While hunting for seedlings of *Taxus,* the native yew, I came across this primula flowering under the protection of an upturned stump, soil and mosses overhanging it and shielding it from the wet snow. I came upon it so suddenly it made me think of a song about a young girl seeking shelter in winter who was turned away. When she died she was buried, and from then on flowers grew on the spot where she lay. So pristine, so vigorous, and so full of life was this primula. But primulas are amazing plants that can flower in snowy weather or during warm fall days when nights can drop below -15°C. They abound in the Himalayas and are, to many, the most typical flower of this mountain region. I found them flowering over ten months of the year in Bhutan, not a bad feat when winters can be so cold and dry, and bare of other succulent plant growth for at least three months of the year. ✳

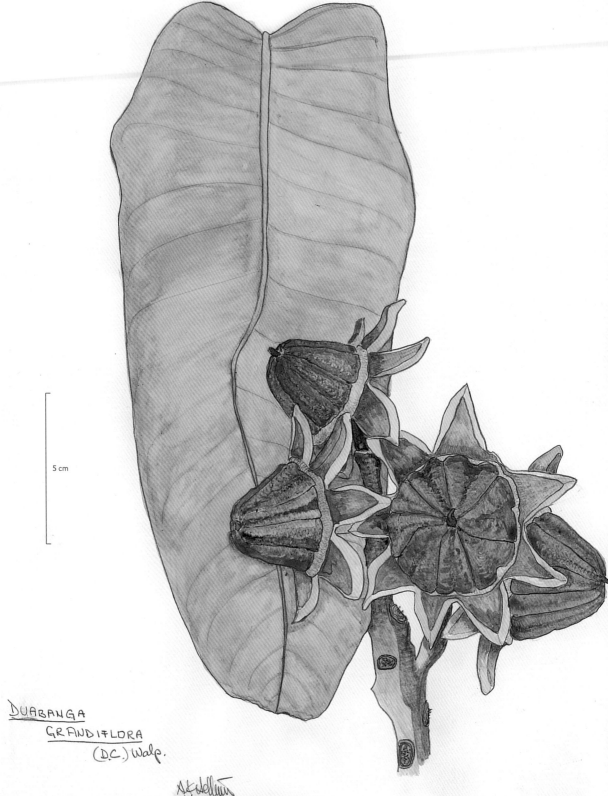

5 cm

DUABANGA
GRANDIFLORA
(D.C.) Walp.

February 18, 1989
From Phuntsholing area
Bhutan

Time to warm up

It was during February 1989 that I could not stand the cold any longer and went down to Phuntsholing to thaw out. Lower reaches of Bhutan lie at or about 300 m above sea level and are much warmer than Thimphu in winter. While there I painted fruits and leaves of *Duabanga grandiflora*. This is a large tree, up to 30 m tall, which is used for lumber and for tea-chests (Mabberley, 1987). ✻

Invaders of the Dragon Kingdom

Solanum kashianum is a member of the nightshade family, and both cattle and humans avoid it. It grows along the roads coming up into the highlands of Bhutan from India. It is an invader.

In February, when other plants are mostly dormant or semi-dormant, the colour of its fruit brightens the disturbed and dull roadsides both above and below Gedu. Gedu is a small place on the road between Phuntsholing and Thimphu, just above the first steep and precipitous drive north and up from the lowlands.

The fruits are green to start with, and they slowly turn yellow. At one stage, these small tomatoes are yellow except for green veins radiating out from their bases. *Solanum's* leaves and stems are thorny, and the recurved spines grab onto your pant leg or a cow's hairy leg and hold on for the ride. Fruits get shaken off in this kind of contact, and they litter the roadsides, where wandering cattle tread them into the gravel and spread them with their hooves. Only climate will stop this plant on its march into the mountains. The fruits turn brown when they rot on the plant, and they fall to earth in a mush where the seeds can germinate in place.

The plants have not yet inhabited many sites away from the roads in Bhutan, but in time wild places will become homes to *Solanum kashianum*. Ignored and patient, the plant winds its way. It is like some unpleasant people I have met. They are left alone, people shun them, and yet slowly they become very well ensconced in new environments, doing what they know best.

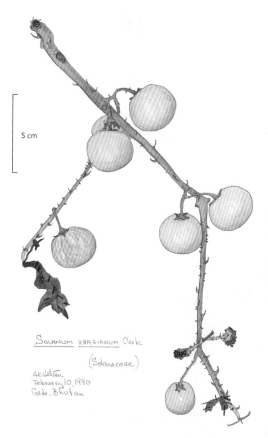

5 cm

Solanum khasianum Clarke

(Solanaceae)

A Hallum
February 10, 1990
Gedu, Bhutan

✻ *Duabanga grandiflora* (Roxb. ex DC.) Walp.

✻ *Solanum kashianum* Clarke [*Solanum torvum* Swartz?]

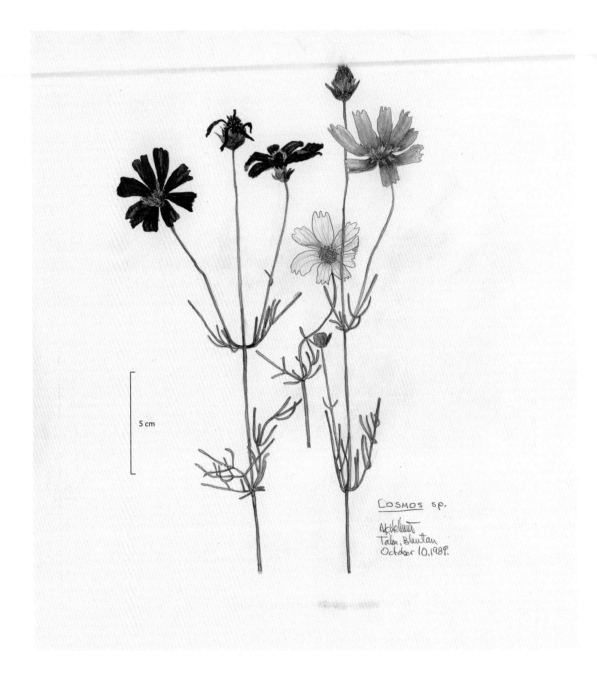

COSMOS sp.

At Helvetir
Talen, Bhutan
October 10, 1989.

There is another plant that has invaded Bhutan recently. It is of the genus *Cosmos*, and it is a member of the composite family, like asters and dandelions. It is naturalized in Bhutan, where it grows in waste fields and along the trails everywhere, signifying that it spreads by the help of man and animals. It spreads from here into the surrounding countryside, flowering in mauve, pink, red and white. ✳

Cosmos sp. Cav.

One drink too many

One grey and dismal day in mid-February 1990 we made a trip by four-wheel-drive vehicle up the Mo *Chu* to the road's end north of Punakha. Here people leave on their two-day walks to the holy place called Gaza and its hot springs. We were looking for tree seedlings to illustrate for a book on seedling identification (Tshering and Hellum, 1990), intended to help forest workers identify regenerating trees.

The greyness of the day and the clouds threatened to bring rain, but there was none, only worries of rain like the worries of the farmer fearing rain before harvest. Despite the wind and cold, it still was by far milder here than in the Thimphu valley 1,000 m higher up and in the next valley to the west. When we reached the end of the road the people we had given a ride to got out, opened their pots and pans, and fed everyone around with hot stew and *arra*, an alcoholic drink made from rice. The chilis in the stew were hot enough to burn throats, and the *emedatse* brought sweat to my brow.

The *arra* made heads swim a little, and second cups were guaranteed to make people sing. It didn't take long before I started to hum to myself.

As we drove back along the muddy and rough road, after having left the hikers behind with their children, women, old men and belongings, we came to a halt where a truck barred the road. Men were loading it up with dead wood from the forest: firewood for Punakha, probably. They asked us to wait, and I sauntered on ahead on foot, looking for more seedlings, and collecting for the local herbarium some of the mosses and lichens growing in abundance on the exposed mineral soil of the road. All along this road these beautiful lobelias (*Lobelia pyramidalis*) grew in profusion, hanging over the road in massive stands, drooping with moisture from the last night's rain. The plants looked like massive goldenrods, except that the flowers were purple and differently shaped.

The arra made heads swim a little,
and second cups were guaranteed
to make people sing.
It didn't take long before
I started to hum to myself.

While poking around along the road I got bothered by all the calves bleating for their mothers. There were a lot of them, and they disturbed the peace for me. I started to bleat back at them, feeling totally uninhibited about it because of the *arra*.

At one point I stopped to straighten my back only to find an older man and a young boy staring intently at me. I felt acute embarrassment when the young boy said in very good English, "What are you doing?"

I was lost for a good answer and simply said, without thinking, "Why can't your cows understand me? I am telling them to stop making so much noise. I have been calling and calling to them."

The boy looked startled, looking at me with his eyes wide open. He turned to the older man and said something in Dzongkha. Then they both walked away very quickly down the road looking back every so often, I presume, to make certain I was not following them.

Closing the bag I headed back to the truck to get away from the whole embarrassment. The road had just been cleared and we could proceed towards Punakha and home. As we passed the herders farther down the road I waved sheepishly to them and they waved back, smiling openly. What were they thinking at that moment? I wonder. ✳

No good. Kill cow.

"Good morning," said the young man who came to check on what I was doing sitting in the grass painting. When he saw the plant I was holding, he seemed judgemental: "No good. Kill cow, kill me, kill everything," he said firmly. But he did not stay long, once he was satisfied about what I was doing. But every other person who came by on the trail to Punakha said the same words. Those who could not speak English passed the message to those who could. Everyone knew the plant, everyone knew its powers. The plant was *Pieris formosa*.

This was a strange late-January morning anyway, because of a small boy who came by. He had been sent out to fetch some wood for his mother. She stood in the doorway of her house shouting to him to move on. But he was very interested in what was happening with the plant, until he noticed the hairs in my nose. He had to inspect further, and put his head only inches from mine, peering into my nose as if he were a doctor. I could not see what I was doing any more. I looked at him. He was still puzzling over the hairs when his mother invaded the scene and scared him off, but having scared the boy off she sat down and started to talk to me in Dzongkha. When that didn't work she asked, "You alone?" I said I was. She said, "Family?"

I answered, "Not here."

Pointing to her house, she asked, "Tea?"

So I said, "Husband?" and she shook her head. "Sisters?" No. "Brothers?" No. "Parents?" No. Then she asked, "Lonely?" and that really started me concentrating on my drawing.

She left finally when the boy came back with a few sticks in his hand. She spoke sharply to him and walked him back to the house, looking back at me once or twice before closing the door.

Lobelia pyramidalis Wall.

5 cm

<u>LOBELIA PYRAMIDALIS</u>
Wallich

(Campanulaceæ)

A.K.Hellums
February 16, 1990
MoChu valley
N. of Phunakha, Bhutan

90

5 cm

PIERIS FORMOSA (Wallich)
D. Don.

A.S. Hellum
January 22, 1989
Pangse Zampa
trail to Punakha
Bhutan.

It wouldn't have been so bad if that had been the end of it, but there were others too who came to ask and discuss things. Soon it seemed like half the country was sitting there in a huge circle around me. I was the excuse for a village gathering, for no one seemed to notice me anymore. They were all talking among themselves—all except one old man, that is, who took great interest in my backpack. He started to rummage in it, and brought out a sweater and an orange, a bar of chocolate and my water bottle. He unscrewed the top and sniffed the contents. No *arra*? Then he put everything back into the sack, all without saying a word.

When I say that painting helps me concentrate I do not mean to say I can ignore everything that happens around me when I paint. The attention I received this day was very good for prac-tising meditation, but even if it did me some good, I am not certain it helped the painting. ❃

I had spent two years in Bhutan
and spring was again around the corner.

❧ *Pieris formosa* (Wallich) D. Don

Reflections

ABOVE ALL, MY TWO YEARS IN BHUTAN TAUGHT ME about silence and listening. My life before Bhutan had been so busy, so crowded with duties and passions and noise, that I had become completely submerged in my *samsara*. Do this, do that, say this, don't say that, go here, go there. Why isn't this done? And what about that? The litany was deafening. If one word describes life in Bhutan for me it is silence. It took a long time for this silence to find passage into my subconscious.

Every story in this book brought a different kind of silence. I had the opportunity to interact with people and nature on my own terms, in my own way. It was surprisingly liberating for a Westerner like myself to be left alone to think and respond without expectations. For me it was startling and rejuvenating.

Some people say that Bhutan is the "Last Shangri-La," but for me Bhutan was a land of hundreds of Shangri-Las, where every alpine meadow, every rocky trail into high country or through old forest was a Shangri-La, and every human encounter a new adventure.

Bhutan has solitude, and dynamic, mystical places filled with fog and wind, rain, snow and ice. These strong influences helped me observe my surroundings without wanting to shut them out; I could enjoy them and feel peaceful inside because I need not get involved.

I was told at the time that Bhutan has only about 700,000 people. That is all. And I think this has a lot to do with the tranquillity that I found there.

In addition, there is something about Bhutan that is haunting, because it shows signs everywhere of humanity's caring and supplication to powers beyond understanding. There are more than 2,000 Buddhist temples in Bhutan, and so many men are in monastic service that I saw them everywhere. They participate in most daily-life routines. Whenever I chose to raise my eye to the high hills anywhere I saw prayer flags waving or snapping in the winds that never seem to stop their restless travel. I heard the chanting of prayers at markets and the horns bugling at special events. Young and old hands were everywhere counting beads and twirling prayer wheels. Houses were decorated with beautiful symbols of good luck (Hasrat, 1980).

I found Bhutan's people curious and open to outsiders. Both characteristics tended to draw people together. Such pulling together is much harder to find in crowded places where individual space is scarce. And because I came from a distant culture, I felt freer and more unencumbered with the trappings of living in Bhutan. My life in Bhutan was relatively and immeasurably simpler than at home in Canada.

The impressive beauty and power of the land itself added to my awareness of my surroundings in Bhutan. Every mountain place has beauty and power, but Bhutan had more beauty and more power of landscape than any other place I had ever seen.

When Westerners come to Bhutan determined to accomplish certain things within certain times, I shuddered. When I saw foreigners synchronize their watches before entering Bhutan, I wanted to laugh and cry at the same time. When I heard foreigners express desires for comforts of living that Bhutan could not offer, I realized how long and hard the road is for foreigner and Bhutanese alike.

I came to appreciate the need of understanding before acting. "Complete" understanding, I was told, comes to the enlightened person when he or she is so in tune with the environment that words become redundant: neither written nor spoken words are necessary any longer. Even though I was never able to concentrate deeply enough to see the plant that some Bhutanese claim to see while in deep meditation, I learned to concentrate on painting plants to maintain my contact with simple things from the earth.

This focus on simple things also made me much more aware of people than I had been before. This is what made it possible to feel so much closer to the people of Bhutan than I felt to Westerners.

One evening in Shemgang, in south-central Bhutan, while sitting and sipping a local brew through a grass straw stuck into millet mash in a bamboo container, I peeked out between the boards in the wall of the little house. I could see Orion. It was my Orion that night, bright and shining in a sky so full of stars. There was not one light from any building or car anywhere that could weaken the splendour of that night. It was my Orion just as it belonged to the people I sat with: my colleagues Wijnand and Bertine, Rinchen and Lungthen. The muted talk all about me was in Dzongkha: my mind was free to dream. This is what Bhutan gave me, space to be myself, to listen to the world around me and to dream. ❊

It has been very difficult to return to my own culture after having been immersed in Bhutan's. I hang suspended, yet I feel very fortunate, and I listen more now to the winds and the rain than I did before.

Appendix

Additional species of Bhutan

MANY OF THE SPECIES OF BHUTAN have not been seen outside of the country, and only a very few botanists have been allowed into Bhutan to review its plant life. The images that follow will provide a broader representation of the diverse flora of Bhutan. ✳

Note that nomenclature is constantly changing. I have named these plants according to the authorities in the late 1980s; the naming may have since changed in some instances.

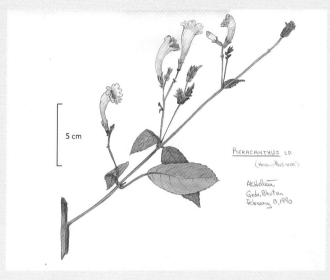

ACANTHACEAE, *Pteracanthus* sp.

BALSAMINACEAE, *Impatiens falcifer*

BERBERIDACEAE | BORAGINACEAE | CAMPANULACEAE

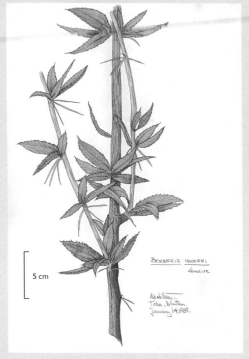

BERBERIDACEAE, *Berberis hookeri*

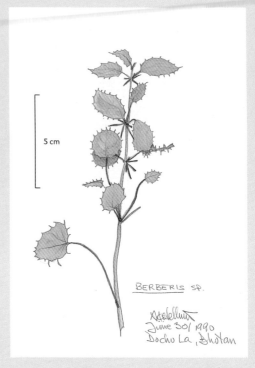

BERBERIDACEAE, *Berberis* sp.

BORAGINACEAE, *Cynoglossum* sp.

CAMPANULACEAE, *Asyneuma thomsonii*

CAPRIFOLIACEAE | CELASTRACEAE | COMMELINACEAE

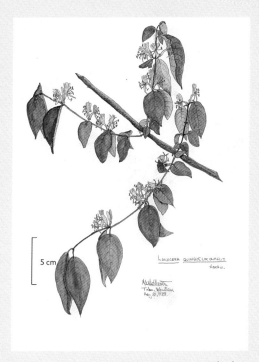

CAPRIFOLIACEAE, *Lonicera quinquelocularis*

CAPRIFOLIACEAE, *Viburnum cylindricum*

CELASTRACEAE, *Euonymus grandiflorus*

COMMELINACEAE, *Cyanotis vaga*

COMPOSITAE

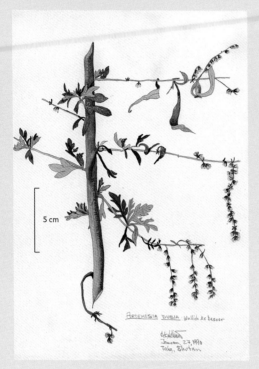

COMPOSITAE, *Artemisia dubia*

COMPOSITAE, *Aster albescens*

COMPOSITAE, *Gerbera gossypina*

COMPOSITAE, *Senecio chrysanthemoides*

Dipsacaceae | Elaeagnaceae | Ephedraceae

DIPSACACEAE, *Dipsacus inermis*

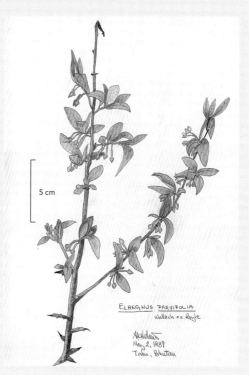

ELAEAGNACEAE, *Elaeagnus parvifolia*

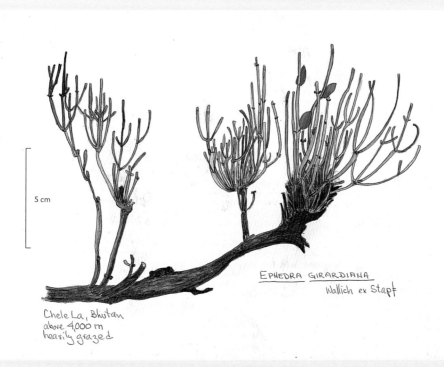

EPHEDRACEAE, *Ephedra girardiana*

ERICACEAE

ERICACEAE, *Gaultheria semi-infera* (fall)

ERICACEAE, *Gaultheria semi-infera* (summer)

ERICACEAE

ERICACEAE, *Lyonia villosa*

ERICACEAE, *Rhododendron barbatum*

ERICACEAE, *Rhododendron cinnabarinum*

ERICACEAE, *Rhododendron virgatum*

EUPHORBIACEAE | FAGACEAE

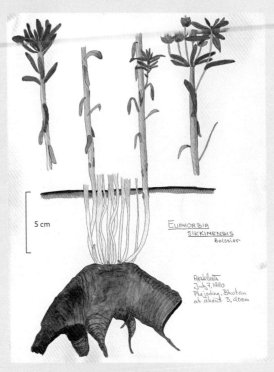

EUPHORBIACEAE, *Euphorbia sikkimensis*

FAGACEAE, *Lithocarpus fenestratus*

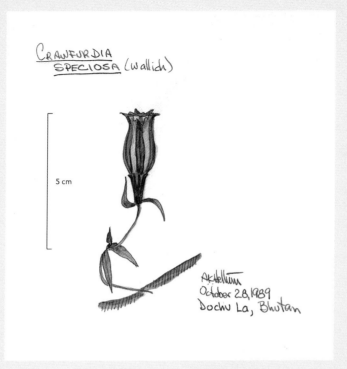

GENTIANACEAE, *Crawfurida speciosa*

GENTIANACEAE, *Gentiana pedicellata*

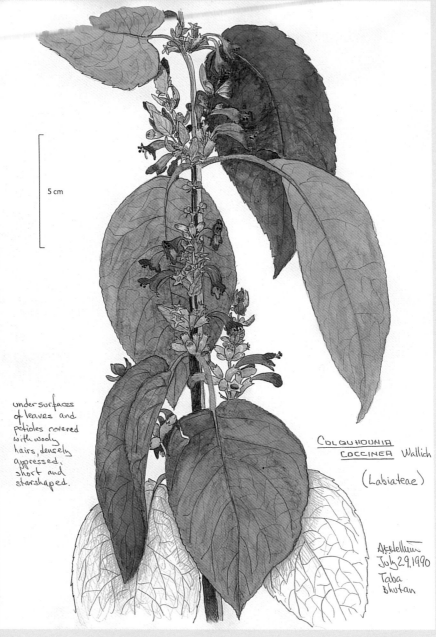

5 cm

under-surfaces
of leaves and
petioles covered
with wooly
hairs, densely
appressed,
short and
star-shaped.

COLQUHOUNIA
COCCINEA Wallich

(Labiateae)

Akstellium
July 29, 1990
Taba
Bhutan

LABIATAE, *Colquhounia coccinea*

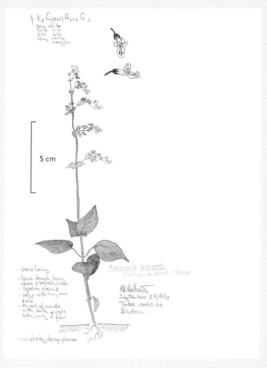

LABIATAE, *Rabdosia rugosa*

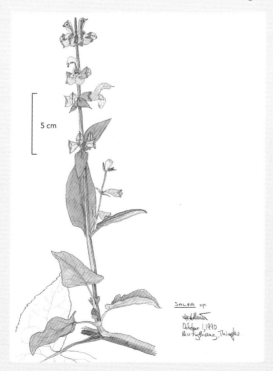

LABIATAE, *Salvia* sp.

LAURACEAE

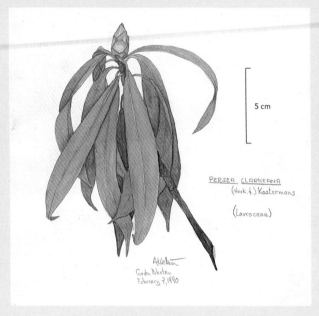

LAURACEAE, *Persea clarkeana*

LAURACEAE, *Persea odoratissima*

LEGUMINOSAE, *Crotalaria capitata*

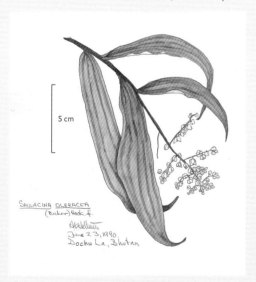

LILIACEAE, *Smilacina oleracea*

Leguminosae, *Indigofera hebepetala*

Liliaceae, *Theropogon pallidus*

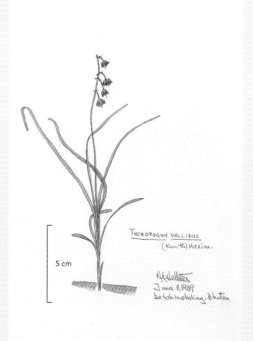

MAGNOLIACEAE | MYRSINACEAE

MAGNOLIACEAE, *Alcimandra cathcartii*

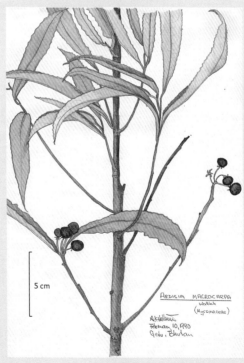

MYRSINACEAE, *Ardisia macrocarpa*

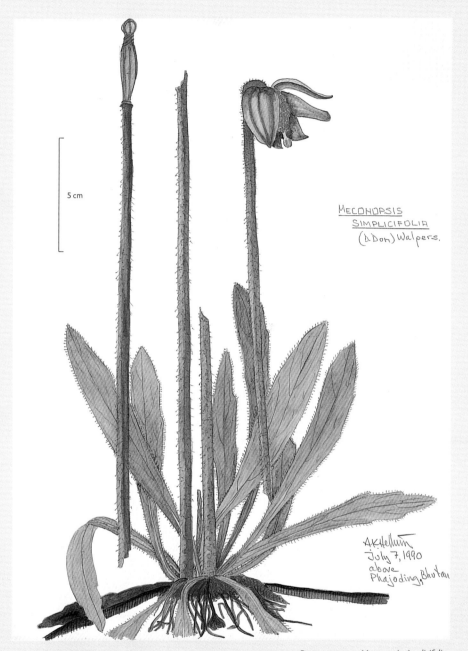

MECONOPSIS
SIMPLICIFOLIA
(D.Don) Walpers.

5 cm

A.K.Hellum
July 7, 1990
above
Phajoding, Bhutan

Papaveraceae, *Meconopsis simplicifolia*

PINACEAE | PLUMBAGINACEAE | PRIMULACEAE

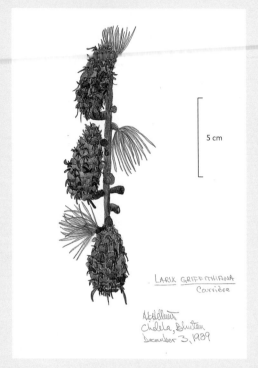

5 cm

LARIX GRIFFITHIANA
Carrière

A.K.Stellman
Chdela, Bhutan
December 3, 1989

PINACEAE, *Larix griffithiana*

5 cm

PICEA SPINULOSA
(Griff.) Henry

A.K.Stellman
March 10, 1989,
Toba, Bhutan

PINACEAE, *Picea spinulosa*

5 cm

CERATOSTIGMA sp.

A.K.Stellman
Chang La Gompa
Paro River Valley
Bhutan
October 21, 1989.

PLUMBAGINACEAE, *Ceratostigma* sp.

5 cm

Primula
denticulata
Smith

Gidakom Valley,
Bhutan
February 5, 1989.

PRIMULACEAE, *Primula denticulata*

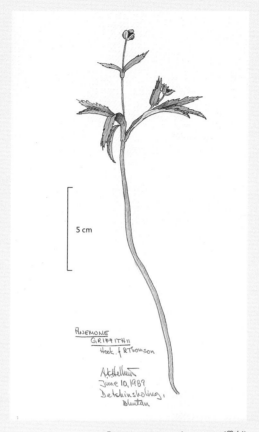

RANUNCULACEAE, *Anemone griffithii*

RANUNCULACEAE, *Oxygraphis endlicheri*

ROSACEAE

FRAGARIA NUBICOLA
(Hook. f.) Lacaita

A.K.Hellum
June 3, 1989
above Taksa, Bhutan

ROSACEAE, *Fragaria nubicola*

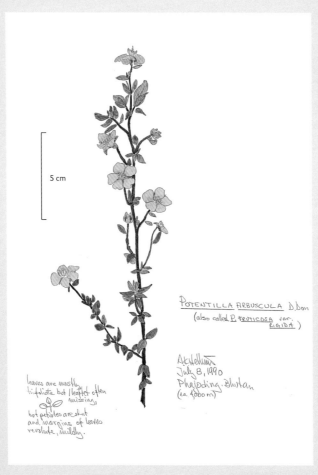

POTENTILLA ARBUSCULA D.Don
(also called P. FRUTICOSA var.
RIGIDA)

A.K.Hellum
July 8, 1990
Phajoding, Bhutan
(ca 4000m)

leaves are mostly
trifoliate but leaflet often
missing;

but petioles are short
and margins of leaves
revolute, mildly.

ROSACEAE, *Potentilla arbuscula*

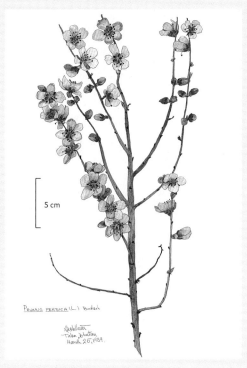

ROSACEAE, *Prunus persica*

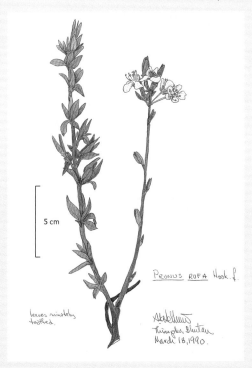

ROSACEAE, *Prunus rufa*

Rosaceae

5 cm

Rosa sericea Lindley

ADMcKellen
May 2, 1989
Taba, Bhutan

ROSACEAE, *Rosa sericea* (spring)

5 cm

Rosa sericea Lindley
"Sew Shing" (Dz.)

ADMcKellen
June 17, 1989
Taba, Bhutan

ROSACEAE, *Rosa sericea* (summer)

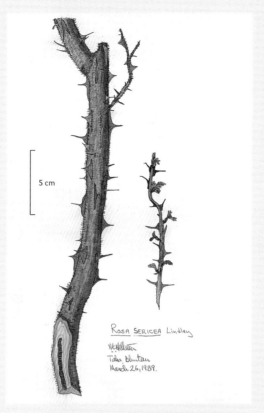

Rosa sericea Lindley

Tashelhum
Taba, Bhutan
March 26, 1989.

ROSACEAE, *Rosa sericea* (winter)

SIBBALDIA PARVIFLORA
Willdenow

$*K_5 C_5 \underset{yellow}{} A_{10} G(\underline{5})$

Tashelhum
March 19, 1989
Taba, Bhutan

ROSACEAE, *Sibbaldia parviflora*

Scrophulariaceae

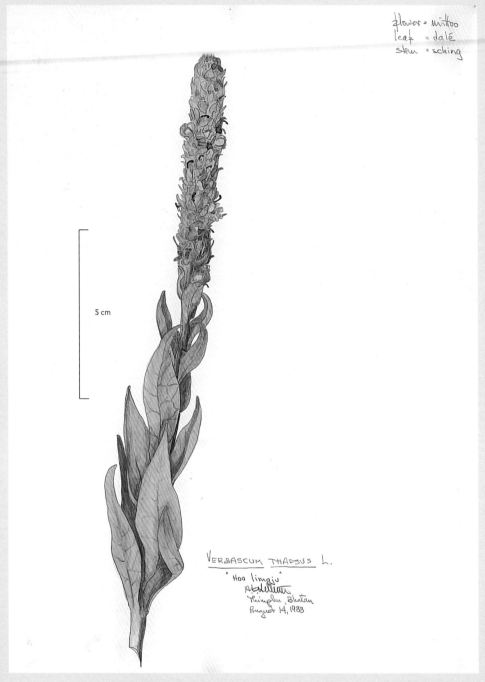

flower = mirtoo
leaf = dalé
stem = sching

5 cm

Verbascum thapsus L.

"Hoo limgiu"

Thimphu, Bhutan
August 14, 1988

Scrophulariaceae, *Verbascum thapsus*

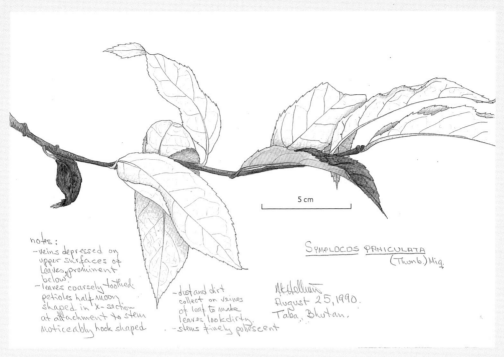

notes:
- veins depressed on upper surfaces of leaves, prominent below.
- leaves coarsely toothed, petioles half moon shaped in x-section at attachment to stem noticeably hook shaped

- dust and dirt collect on veins of leaf to make leaves look dirty.
- stems finely pubescent

5 cm

SYMPLOCOS PANICULATA
(Thunb.) Miq.

McCollum
August 25, 1990.
Taba, Bhutan.

SYMPLOCACEAE, *Symplocos paniculata*

THYMELAEACEAE, *Daphne bholua*

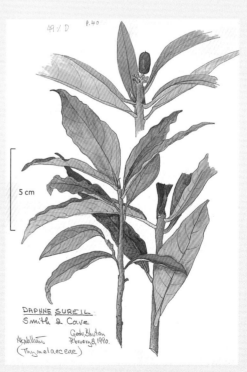

THYMELAEACEAE, *Daphne sureil*

5 cm

ROSCOEA PURPUREA
Smith

A.K. Wellum
Detchinsholing, Bhutan
June 11, 1989.

ZINGIBERACEAE, *Roscoea purpurea*

Bibliography

Aris, M. 1982. *Views of Medieval Bhutan: The Diary and Drawings of Samuel Davis, 1793.* London: Serindra Publishing with Smithsonian Institution Press.

Collister, P. 1987. *Bhutan and the British.* N.p.: Serindra Publishers with Belitha Press.

Das, N. 1974. *The Dragon Country: The General History of Bhutan.* Bombay: Orient Longman Ltd.

Development Co-operation: Bhutan 1988 Report. 1989. Thimphu: UNDP.

Development Co-operation: Bhutan 1995 Report. 1997. Thimphu: UNDP.

Grierson, A.C.J. and D.G. Long. 1983–91. *Flora of Bhutan: Including a Record of Plants from Sikkim.* 2 vols. Edinburgh: Royal Botanic Garden.

Hasrat, B.J. 1980. *History of Bhutan: Land of the Peaceful Dragon.* Thimphu: Bhutan Department of Education.

Hickman, K. 1987. *Dreams of the Peaceful Dragon: A Journey into Bhutan.* London: Victor Gollancz Ltd.

An Introduction to Traditional Medicine in Bhutan. 1989. Bhutan Department of Health.

Mabberley, D.J. 1987. *The Plant Book.* Cambridge: Cambridge University Press.

Polunin, O. and A. Stainton. 1984. *Flowers of the Himalayas.* Delhi: Oxford University Press.

Ross, R. 1992. *Dancing with a Ghost: Exploring Indian Reality.* Markham: Octopus Books.

Stainton, A. 1988. *Flowers of the Himalayas: A Supplement.* Delhi: Oxford University Press.

Tshering, S. and A.K. Hellum. 1990. *Identification of Some Tree Seedlings in Bhutan.* Bangkok: Craftsman Press.•

★Copies of this booklet can be obtained
from the Food and Agriculture Organization (F.A.O.)
of the United Nations from:

Maliwan Mansion
Phra Afit Road
Banglampoo, Bangkok
10200 Thailand

as long as supplies last.

About the Author

A.K. Hellum was born in Norway in 1933. He later emigrated to Canada to study forestry at the University of British Columbia. He completed his studies at the University of Michigan and went on to teach silviculture at the University of Alberta in Edmonton until 1988. He has travelled around the world consulting on forestry matters such as seed technology, seedling identification and silviculture.

Dr. Hellum is widely published as both a scholar and a painter, and his art has been exhibited across Canada and in the US, Norway, and Bhutan. For him, painting is both practical and inspiring: "My skills in drawing and painting are useful in my consulting work. But beauty in nature has always caught my eye, and painting gives me a unique chance to study this beauty in meditative silence." ✳